D1179738

MEMORIES OF MY CHILDHOOD

Selma Lagerlöf

Ett barns memoarer

(Mårbacka II)

Stockholm
Albert Bonniers Förlag

Reproduction of the title page of the first Swedish edition
of *Memories of My Childhood*, with an old family photo-
graph of the author as a little girl.

MEMORIES
OF MY CHILDHOOD

Further Years at Mårbacka

SELMA LAGERLÖF

TRANSLATED BY
VELMA SWANSTON HOWARD

DOUBLEDAY, DORAN & COMPANY, INC.
GARDEN CITY 1934 NEW YORK

KRAUS REPRINT CO.
Millwood, New York
1975

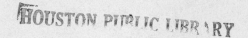
Library of Congress Cataloging in Publication Data

Lagerlöf, Selma Ottiliana Lovisa, 1858-1940.
    Memories of my childhood.

      Translation of Ett barns memoarer.
      Reprint of the ed. published by Doubleday, Garden
City, N. Y.
      1. Lagerlöf, Selma Ottiliana Lovisa, 1858-1940—
Biography.   I. Title.
PT9770.A25   1975   839.7'3'72 [B]   75-5996
ISBN 0-527-54010-2

CONTENTS

I. ALINE LAURELL *P. 1*

II. WAITING FOR THE POST *P. 9*

III. THE VOW *P. 20*

IV. GÅRDSJÖ *P. 46*

V. HERRESTAD *P. 52*

VI. FEAR *P. 56*

VII. THE CARD GAME *P. 63*

VIII. THE MARSEILLAISE *P. 70*

IX. FORTY DEGREES BELOW ZERO *P. 82*

X. MAJA RÅD *P. 95*

XI. GOING TO CHURCH *P. 103*

XII. THE KISS *P. 113*

XIII. THE BALL AT SUNNE *P. 127*

XIV. ELIN LAURELL *P. 139*

XV. PASTOR UNGER *P. 149*

v

XVI. THE EASTER WITCH *P. 163*

XVII. ANNA LAGERLÖF *P. 174*

XVIII. UNCLE SCHENSON *P. 181*

XIX. THE POND *P. 193*

XX. AGRIPPA PRÄSTBERG *P. 220*

XXI. AT THE PIER *P. 236*

XXII. THE WELL *P. 245*

XXIII. THE MARKET FAIR *P. 269*

XXIV. THE "EARTHQUAKE" *P. 281*

MEMORIES OF MY CHILDHOOD

I

ALINE LAURELL

We HAVE a nice new governess at Mårbacka. Her name is Aline Laurell. She comes from Karlstad, where her father had been chief surveyor. While he lived the family were said to be well-to-do; but after his death they became very poor. So Aline's maternal aunt, Fru Unger of West Ämtervik, arranged with Mamma and Papa for her niece to live with us and give Anna and me lessons in music and French.

Aline brought with her a little sister whose name is Emma and who is only ten years old. She is to live here, too, and study with Aline. It is plain that they were once rich, for Emma has a lot of fine embroidered pantalettes, which have come down to her from Aline and her other sisters. We have never had such things at Mårbacka.

On Sunday mornings Emma tries to baste these pantalettes to her drawers, and a dreadful time she has of it! Some are too wide and some too long, and, when she puts them on, it happens quite often that one leg hangs down to her foot while the other hardly comes to her knee. We do not think her pantalettes are pretty, especially when they hang unevenly; but Emma probably thinks that since she has a whole bureau drawer filled with them, and they are so beautifully embroidered, she ought to wear them.

The autumn Aline came to live with us I was in Stockholm attending the Orthopedic Institute. I lived with Uncle Oriel Afzelius and Aunt Georgina at number 7 Clara Strandgata. I had been away the whole winter and did not meet Aline until my return, the following spring. Glad as I was to be back again, at the same time I felt uneasy because of the new governess. For I thought that all governesses were old, and ugly, and cross.

When I came from Stockholm I wore a Panama hat with a blue-and-white band around the crown and trimmed with a white plume and buckle. I had on a blue summer coat with metal buttons and a frock of blue-and-white organdie Aunt Georgina had ordered for me; so I looked quite smart when I came home. And besides, I had improved so much at the Orthopedic Institute that my lameness was scarcely perceptible. Moreover, I had grown taller and was not so thin and pale as when I went away. On the contrary, I was quite plump and rosy. My hair was worn in a braid down my back instead of being done up round my ears in two buns. In fact, I was so changed they hardly knew me at home. They all declared it was an entirely new Selma who had come back to them.

When I saw Aline I was surprised to find her so young and pretty. I took to her from the first. But Aline must have thought me a pert little Stockholm miss, a spoiled and affected child.

Having been away so long, I had much to tell, and I talked on and on. I had been to the opera, I told them, and to the Royal Dramatic Theatre, and also to the Theatre Intime. I had stood in Deer Park on the first day of May, and had seen King Charles XV and Queen Louise and the little princess. And I told them that Louise Thyselius, who was the prettiest young girl in Stockholm, had gone to the same institute that I had, and her I had seen every day; that the house in which Uncle Oriel lived was owned by a French duke whose name was d'Otrante. The duke had many fine horses and carriages, and his father had been something big and terrible in the French Revolution. I showed them all the books Uncle and Aunt had given me for Christmas, and boasted of the children's Christmas party at Merchant Glosemeyer's to which Elin and Allan and I had been invited. There we were allowed to strip the Christmas tree, and we each got a bagful of sweets to take home. Then I described Leja's Toy Shop where I had seen such heaps of toys. And I had seen chocolate cigars, too, and a red, blue, and green fountain which was called Kalospinterokromatokrene.

Aline Laurell sat quietly listening to it all but offered no comment. She must have said to herself, "What a sophisticated child this Selma is who has just returned from Stockholm!" The worst of it was that I spoke all the while with a Stockholm accent. I was not conscious of this myself, but Aline probably thought I affected it, and that one who was born in Värmland should not be ashamed to speak her mother tongue.

I flung out such names as Drottninggatan, Berzelii Park, Blasieholmen, Slussen; and talked of the Royal Guard and the Royal Palace; of going to the Catholic church; of seeing "Saint George and the Dragon" and "The Last Judgment" at Storkyrkan, the great cathedral where Royalty worshipped. I had read, at Uncle Oriel's, all of Walter Scott's novels and had studied with a good teacher, who said I would make an excellent teacher myself when I grew up.

And all this Aline Laurell had to listen to. I daresay she thought that she could never be friends with a girl who was so conceited.

As there were only a few weeks more until the summer holidays, when Aline and Emma would be going to Karlstad to spend the holidays with their

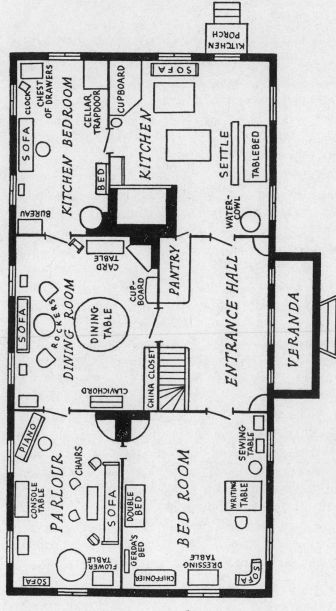

Ground-floor Plan of the Manor House at Mårbacka

mother, Papa said it was not worth while to begin lessons with Aline now. So I was free to do as I liked until autumn.

It was fun to go into the kitchen and chat with the housekeeper; to look at Gerda's dolls; to play with the dogs and the kittens; to read aloud to Mamma from Nösselt's *Popular History for Women*, and to help Aunt Lovisa set out plants in the garden. But when I had been at home a couple of days I went up to the nursery one morning during school hours—not to study, or do sums, or write, but only to see how the children behaved.

Aline was hearing Anna and Emma in catechism, and Anna was reading the long, difficult passage about "the heathen who have not the law." When Anna had finished, Aline talked to her and Emma about conscience, explaining the whole difficult passage so clearly that Anna and Emma understood the meaning perfectly. So did I. Aline is right in saying, if we always do as our conscience bids us we will have no cause for regret.

At eleven o'clock the lesson was over, and Anna and Emma were allowed ten minutes to run out and play, but I remained in the nursery. I went up to Aline, my cheeks burning, and asked her, in a voice so low it was scarcely audible, if she would help me send twenty-four skillings to Läxå station, to the railway guard's wife who lived there.

"Why, certainly," said Aline. "What is her name?"

"I don't know," I said. "But when the train I was on came to Läxå station it ran over a guard. I didn't see him, but some of the passengers said he was cut in two."

"Oh!" gasped Aline. "And you feel sorry for his poor wife."

"She shrieked so horribly as she ran toward the station. You never heard such shrieks! They also said that she was poor, and had many children."

"Now I remember reading about it in the newspaper," said Aline. "But didn't they take up a collection?"

"Yes, they did. A conductor came into our carriage and asked if we did not wish to help the guard's wife. There were many who gave, but I gave nothing."

"Had you no money?"

"I had two twelve-skilling pieces, but I intended to buy burnt almonds and other nuts with the money when I came to Karlstad, so as to have something to take home to Anna and Gerda. It all happened so quickly, you see, and the conductor was in such a hurry he didn't notice me. So I did not take out the money."

"And now you would like to send it?"

"Yes. If you will only help me. I bought no burnt almonds at Karlstad, so I still have the money. I felt so guilty as I sat in the railway carriage, for I thought everyone in the compartment was looking at me and wondering why I had not given something. And I have been ashamed of myself ever since I came home, and now I would like so much to send the money to the guard's wife."

Aline turned her large grey eyes upon me. "Why have you not talked with your mother about this?" she asked.

"I thought I wouldn't speak of it to anyone; but I heard what you said about conscience."

"Well, then," Aline said thoughtfully, "I'll help you."

I went after my two twelve-skilling coins and gave them to her.

Since then Aline and I have been the best of friends. I can tell her things which I never mention to anyone else. Once I told her about a lovely story I had read when I was seven years old entitled *Oceola*, and that I decided, after reading that book, to write stories when I grew up.

II
WAITING FOR THE POST

We think it great fun to go for the post on Sundays. Only we big girls, Anna, Emma Laurell, and I, are permitted to go. We steal away before Gerda awakens from her midday nap, for she would be sure to cry if we did not take her along. Gerda is only six, you see, and too small to jump a ditch or climb a fence without help.

Sometimes Nurse Maja wants to come along, as she finds it too dull to stay at home all day Sunday. Maja is Gerda's nurse, and she has no orders from Mamma or Papa to look after us. Anna is twelve years old, Emma Laurell is eleven, and I am ten; so we don't need anyone to take care of us. Nurse Maja comes just for the fun of it. She would rather go after the post with Anna and Emma and me than to hang around the woodshed at home and gabble with Lars

Nylund and Magnus Engström. She says those boys talk a lot of nonsense.

Nurse Maja is with us again today, and as we cross the barnyard and go down through the fields past Per of Berlin's cottage, she tells us how it was when she and Lars Nylund and the other small children of Högbergssäter tended sheep at Åsskogen. One time Lars Nylund killed an adder, just as it was ready to bury its fangs in Maja's big toe. Another time Maja had gone down in a bog all the way up to her chin, and she never again would have seen the light of day if Lars Nylund had not come along just then and pulled her out.

To hear Nurse Maja talk of the days when she tended sheep is always so entertaining. But in the most exciting part of the story Anna said that Nurse Maja must be awfully sweet on Lars Nylund. But Maja said it wasn't so; they only played at being sweethearts when they were children. I'm sorry that Anna teased Maja, for now she won't tell us any more.

It was well we left Gerda at home. Think how tired she would have been after a tramp of nearly two miles—she who is only six! Even I get tired, and I'm ten. Not that it is anything for me to walk a mile or two; now that I've had a whole winter of gymnastics at the institute in Stockholm my lame leg is quite strong. But the road from Per of Berlin's cottage to the inn at Högberg is as wet as a marsh. Every time you lift your foot it says "smack." We did not know when we set out that it had been thawing for three days. Anna says we will find that the postillion has been delayed by the bad roads and we'll get no post today. I don't see how Anna can be so sure.

But the first thing we hear, on coming to the inn, is that the postillion has not yet gone by with the post for Mårbacka. Anna thinks we should turn back immediately, but Nurse Maja wonders if we'd better not wait awhile, as Lieutenant Lagerlöf will be disappointed if we come home without the post.

I'm glad Anna finally decides to wait. Now we can go into the parlour of the inn and rest. The hostess puts chairs for us down by the door. Nobody speaks to us, so we sit there quietly and look about the room. Over by the window a large table has been laid, with bread, butter, and cheese, and near it another table with cups and saucers for coffee. In the fireplace are several big coffee urns that bubble and sputter and sometimes boil over. The eldest daughter of the house is busy grinding coffee. Nurse Maja says, under her breath, that nothing smells so good as coffee, especially when you're tired and wet and half frozen. And we think so, too. Anna tells her to hush or the folks at the inn will think we expect them to offer us refreshments. After a little, Nurse Maja goes out to see whether the postillion is in sight yet. She is gone so long that we begin to wonder if she is ever coming back. We feel uneasy as we see so many people gathering outside. Some of them open the door as if about to come in, but when they see us they shake their heads and turn back. We hear the eldest daughter—she who ground the coffee—whisper to her mother: "Are those Mårbacka youngsters never going to leave?" Then Anna whispers to Emma Laurell and me that they are to have some kind of party here and want to be rid of us. We decide to go as soon as Nurse Maja puts in an appearance.

But Nurse Maja does not appear. Anna whispers to Emma Laurell that she thinks Maja has made an appointment to meet Lars Nylund here. That is why she was so eager to come with us. But I can't believe that Nurse Maja is so sly. I sit gazing out of the window, hoping to catch a glimpse of her. Directly opposite me is a stable, in one corner of which is an old stairway. From where I sit only the two lower steps can be seen. On those two steps stand two persons. I can't see who they are, for on one step only a pair of boots and the bottoms of two trouser legs are visible, and on the other all I can see is the hem of a striped skirt and a pair of buckled shoes. They must have a good deal to say to each other, those two, for they have been standing there a long while. I think I know the striped skirt, but it seems mighty strange that Nurse Maja would stand talking to a pair of trousers when she went out to look for the postman. I am about to ask Anna what she thinks of the striped skirt, when the hostess of the inn comes toward us and says in passing—not to us, but as if talking to herself: "Aye, it will be good to hear Paulus Andersson of Sandarne once more."

We sit still and listen. Now she is right behind us, gathering firewood from the bin. "Praised be the Lord, Paulus Andersson is to hold a Gospel meeting in my house this afternoon at four o'clock," she says, and slams the wood down on the hearth. "All who want to stay and listen," she adds, "are welcome. I say, like the Lord Jesus, 'he who comes to me shall not be cast out.' But he who loves the world more than he loves his God must go his way."

We three turn our eyes toward the big grandfather clock. It is exactly five minutes to four. Emma Laurell and I rise to go, but Anna does not move. She motions us to sit down again.

What in the world is Anna thinking of? Does she mean that we are to stay and listen to a Gospel reading? Doesn't she know that Father regards all colporteurs and evangelists as the worst kind of pests? Has she forgotten how many times Papa has said that if any member of his household went to their meetings, he could never darken his door again?

Before I can ask Anna what she means to do, Nurse Maja comes in to tell us we must go at once, as there is to be a Gospel meeting here at four o'clock. But Anna says she will stay.

"You know, Anna," Nurse Maja warns her, "Lieutenant Lagerlöf doesn't want us to listen to any of these gospellers."

"We can't help it if they hold a Bible meeting here while we're waiting for the post," says Anna.

"But I'm afraid to stay," Nurse Maja tells her; "so I think I'll run home alone."

"I have wanted to go home all the while," Anna mutters. (We can see that she is furious at Maja.) "But you made us sit here while you and Lars Nylund were spooning; so now you'll have to take the consequences."

Two young menservants come in to arrange the benches and chairs. That puts an end to the wrangling. When the men have finished, all the people waiting outside crowd into the room, which is soon filled to overflowing. We move our chairs farther back toward the wall and stay. Since Anna is not afraid to stay, it can't hurt the rest of us, we think. We are all very curious to know what goes on at a Gospel meeting.

Then at last comes Paulus Andersson of Sandarne. He looks like a common peasant. I don't see but that he preaches in the usual way. But of course I can't follow his sermon, for I'm thinking all the while of what is to happen when we get home. Anna needn't think it will do any good to tell Papa that we waited for the post. He'll turn us out of our good home anyhow for our disobedience and our curiosity. It will be with us as it had been with Adam and Eve.

What possible excuse can Anna offer for us when we come home? And what will become of us afterward? I suppose we'll have to go out on the highway and beg. Nurse Maja has her parents at Högbergssäter, and Emma Laurell has a mother in Karlstad, but Anna and I have nowhere to go but Mårbacka.

I have often heard Papa say that colporteurs are worse than thieves and murderers, and that they should all be shut up in the Marstrand Fortress. So how can we expect anything from him but to be turned out in the road? It is lucky for Gerda that she is not with us today. She doesn't know how fortunate she is.

Anna gives me a nudge with her elbow, and I see a man standing in the doorway holding a post bag. We slip out quietly and start for home. We are too unhappy and too frightened for words. Not one of us dares speak on the way home.

When we have gone past Per of Berlin's cottage and are crossing the meadow, we see Lina, the tall scullerymaid, waiting for us. Lina, who is always so kind, must have come out to warn us.

"Why are you so late?" she says. "You had no sooner left the house than the Lieutenant heard that the pietists were holding a Gospel meeting this afternoon at the inn, and he has been worrying the whole afternoon because you were gone so long. He was afraid you had all gone over to the pietists."

There is no time to explain. We hurry across the yard and up the entrance steps. Nurse Maja is afraid to go in with us, so she slips in through the kitchen.

But Anna is not afraid. Before we enter the house she cautions us not to tell about Nurse Maja and Lars Nylund, as she doesn't wish to cause Maja any embarrassment. But she does not say that we must be silent about the Gospel meeting. Then, without stopping to remove her wraps, Anna goes straight to the living room, Emma and I timidly following.

The shades have been drawn and the lamp lighted. Mamma and Aline are sitting at the round table, having a game of patience. Aunt Lovisa is seated on the sofa, with Gerda at her side, drawing a little flower for her. Papa sits in the rocking chair, chatting as usual.

Although Anna knows Papa has forbidden us to attend a Gospel meeting, she goes right over to him and holds out the bag.

"Here is the post, Papa."

Papa pretends he doesn't see that we have come.

Anna stands there with the bag, but he goes right on talking to Mamma and Aline.

When Papa acts in this way it is a sure sign that he is angry. Mamma and Aline pause in their game, and Aunt Lovisa stops drawing. None of them says a word. Emma Laurell and I take hold of hands; we are scared almost to death. Anna, however, is fearless and calm.

"The postillion was late on account of the bad roads," she says; "so we had to wait at the inn until five o'clock."

Papa sits rocking in his chair and does not listen to Anna. But now Mamma speaks up:

"Tell me, Anna, what did you do while waiting?"

"We did nothing the first hour—just sat there. Then an evangelist came to the inn and held a prayer meeting. But the moment the postillion came with the post, we left."

"But, Anna, you know that Papa has told you not to listen to any of these pietist preachers."

"Yes," says Anna, "but this one was Paulus of Sandarne, and you know, Mamma, that he is the most dangerous man of them all."

"But, my dear child, must you stop to hear him because he is dangerous?"

"I didn't know there was to be a Gospel meeting in time to leave before the preaching began, and I was afraid he might be so angry with us, if we left just then, that he would come to Mårbacka and rob the house."

Papa suddenly stops rocking. "What is the girl saying?" he mutters. "Has she gone crazy?"

All at once, I see that Aline Laurell is red as a beet. She bends over the cards, her cheeks distended with suppressed laughter. Aunt Lovisa leans back in her sofa corner, laughing so hard that she has to hold her sides.

"There, Gustaf, you see the result of your extravagant statements," says Mamma, her voice betraying her desire to laugh with the others. Then, turning to Anna, she asks, "Who told you that Paulus of Sandarne steals?"

"Papa has always said he is a bigger knave than Robber Lasse-Maja and he ought to be locked up in prison."

And now Emma Laurell and I have to laugh, too; for we knew all the while that Papa only meant that colporteurs and gospel-mongers were as bad as convicts. But we wouldn't have believed that Anna, who has turned twelve, and who is such a sensible girl, would take him so seriously.

Now that we are all laughing, it dawns upon Anna that she has been very stupid. Her lip begins to quiver as if she were going to cry. Then Father rises and takes the post bag from her.

"Well done, Anna," he says. "You are Papa's own

girl. Don't you mind their laughing, for we two are right, you see. Take Emma and Selma with you and lay off your wraps, and put on dry shoes and stockings. Then ask your aunt to give you some almonds and syrup so you can make toffy. You should have some reward for waiting so long for the post."

III
THE VOW

Oh, why doesn't Papa come home? He went away
the day after we had been to the prayer meeting at
the inn and has not been at home since. We miss him
dreadfully. There is no one now who talks to us at
dinner; no one who plays with us in the evening,
after supper. Nurse Maja says he is out collecting
taxes and has only been gone a few weeks; but to us
it seems as though he has been away for months.

Then, one morning, Mamma tells us that Papa is
coming home today, and we are overjoyed. Many
times that day we run out on the porch to watch for
him and to listen for his sleigh bells.

"Don't keep running in and out, children,"
Mamma says, "or you'll catch cold." But we don't
care.

Aline Laurell scolds us because our minds are not

on our lessons. "If I did not know who was coming this afternoon, you would all get bad marks."

Gerda is busy dressing her dolls the whole livelong day. She dresses and undresses and dresses them again; she can't seem to make them fine enough to suit her. Anna and I assure Emma Laurell that Papa has toys for her as well as for us. She doesn't know our papa if she has any doubts about that.

At four o'clock, when lessons for the day are over, Aline tells us we need not read our lessons for tomorrow. She knows, of course, that we couldn't learn them anyhow. Anna, Gerda, and I, and Emma Laurell, too, all rush out to meet Papa. But first we run down to the stable to get the big ram that Johan drove for us last Christmas, and harness him to the sled. The snow is nearly gone, but we know that Papa likes to see us drive the stable ram.

What luck! We have hardly reached the avenue when we hear the jingle of sleigh bells. Now he is coming! We recognize the horse, and the wide sledge, and Magnus the driver, and Papa, himself, in his big wolfskin coat. We barely have time to push and pull the ram out of the way, for he is not sufficiently broken into harness to turn aside when he meets a horse. He plants himself in the middle of the road, rises on his hind legs, and thrusts his head forward, ready to drive the horse into the ditch.

How strange that Papa does not stop to greet us!

I thought he would take Gerda and me into the sleigh, or at least let Gerda ride to the house with him; but Papa only nods his head ever so little and drives by.

We are sorry now that we took the ram out, as we are in a hurry to get to the house, and the ram doesn't know enough to turn round when we pull on the rein. All four of us have to stand on one side of him and push till he understands what he must do. That is why we were too late to receive Papa when he pulled up at the curb. But why he did not wait there for us, we can't understand.

We storm into the hall—no, he isn't here. He must be hiding somewhere. We are about to rush into his room, when the door opens and Mamma comes out.

"Go quietly upstairs, like good children, and stay in the nursery. Papa is ill and must go to bed. He has a high fever." Mamma's voice trembles so as she speaks that we are frightened.

After we have crept upstairs and gone into the nursery, Anna says that she thinks Papa is dying.

In the evening, when we're all in bed, Mamma always comes up to hear our prayers. We say an "Our Father," and "Lord Bless Us and Keep Us," and "God Who Cares for Little Children," and "An Angel Watches over Us." She goes from bed to bed and we each repeat, in turn, the same prayers—first, Anna, then Emma Laurell, then I. Emma Laurell also prays God to bless and keep her mamma and

her brothers and sisters and all good people. But tonight Anna also ends her prayer like Emma: "Dear
Lord, bless and keep my papa and mamma and my
brothers and sisters and all good people."

Anna says that because she wants God to protect
her papa, who is sick. Mamma understands and bends
down and kisses her. Then Mamma goes over to
Emma Laurell, and after Emma has said an "Our
Father," and "Lord Bless Us and Keep Us," and
"God Who Cares for Little Children," and "An
Angel Watches over Us," she prays as usual for her
mamma, her brothers and sisters, and for all good
people, but at the very last she says: "Dear God,
spare good Uncle Lagerlöf, and don't let him die as
You did my papa."

When Emma Laurell has said her prayers, Mamma
bends down and kisses her also. Then she comes over
to my bed. And I say an "Our Father," and "Lord
Bless Us and Keep Us," and "God Who Cares for
Little Children," and "An Angel Watches over
Us"—but I can't say any more. I want to, but
words fail me. Mamma waits a moment, and then
she says:

"Aren't you going to pray God not to take your
papa from you?"

I want to—oh! I want so much to say it, but I
can't.

Mamma waits a little longer. I know she is thinking of all Papa has done for me. It was for my sake he went that time to Strömstad; for my sake, too, that he sent me to Stockholm for a whole winter's treatment at the institute. And yet I can't get a word across my lips. Mamma rises and goes away without kissing me.

But after she has gone I lie thinking that perhaps Papa will die because I did not pray for him. Perhaps God is angry because I did not ask Him to protect my papa, and will take him away! What can I do to show God that I do not want my papa to die?

I have a little gold heart and a small onyx cross which Mamselle Spaak gave me. If I give these mementoes away perhaps God will understand that I do so that my papa may live. But I'm afraid Mamma might object to my parting with these keepsakes. I shall have to think of something else.

The doctor has just been here. Soon after he left, Mamma told us that Papa had inflammation of the lungs. She said that one night while Papa was away from home he had to sleep between damp sheets, which was the most dangerous thing one could do.

Aline Laurell helped Mamma to nurse Papa last night; and today, too, she has spent most of the time in the sickroom. Mamma doesn't know what she would do without Aline, for she is clear-headed and calm. Aunt Lovisa, on the contrary, is so dreadfully

afraid Papa will die that Mamma can't have her in
the sickroom.

After assigning our lessons for the day and giving
us long sums in arithmetic to do, Aline went down to
Papa's room. But she did not come back to see
whether our answers were correct. At last we children,
finding it too dreary to be alone in the nursery, and
so far removed from all the grown-ups, steal downstairs to Aunt Lovisa's room.

Auntie sits at her sewing table reading in a big,
thick book, with Gerda on a low stool at her side—
making a dress for her doll. We three—Anna, Emma
Laurell, and I—crawl up on Auntie's sofa and sit
there quietly. We think it strange that Gerda can
play with her dolls on a day like this. But then Gerda
is too young to understand that her papa is dying.

We feel easier since we came into the kitchen
bedroom. Everyone thinks Aunt Lovisa's room so
cozy. They all say it is a bit of the old Mårbacka.
Here is the wide bed where Grandfather and Grandmother had slept, and there, in the corner, is the tall
grandfather clock, and near it stands the pretty
bureau the clever carpenter at Askersby made for
them from the wood of an old apple tree and old
syringa grown at Mårbacka. The cover on Auntie's
sofa Grandmother made with her own hands, and the
intricate pattern she learned from Aunt Wennervik,

who was married to Grandmother's brother. The chair on which Auntie is sitting was Grandfather's own desk chair, and the mirror on the dresser, with a veil hung over it, was also made at Askersby. The tall wooden urns, filled with dried rose leaves, on either side of the mirror, Auntie bought at the auction at Valsäter, where her sister Anna—she who was married to Uncle Wachenfeldt—had lived.

There is nothing in the kitchen bedroom that Aunt Lovisa would part with except, perhaps, the ugly black trapdoor over the cellar stairs. But when Papa talks of taking it away, Auntie says he'd better let it stay, since it is so old. She would not feel at home in her room if the trapdoor were missing.

On the wall above Aunt Lovisa's bed hangs a picture of a white church in a grove of towering trees; and a low cemetery wall with an iron gate, enclosing a churchyard. That picture, however, is not painted but clipped. It was Aunt Anna Wachenfeldt who wielded the shears. Aunt Lovisa says that picture is so skilfully cut out and pasted together that it is really a work of art! But I think it looks tawdry. Around the mirror there are four small canvases which Auntie herself painted when she was in boarding school at Åmål. One represents a rose, the second a narcissus, the third a carnation, and the fourth a dahlia. These, I think, are very pretty. Aunt Lovisa still has her box of colours and her pencils, but she never paints any more pictures as pretty as these. Auntie also has another picture which hangs above the sofa. It represents a stout boy and a stout girl out rowing in a small round boat into which they can barely squeeze. The whole picture is worked in cross-stitch on canvas. Aline Laurell says that Aunt Lovisa ought to take it out of the frame and make it into a cover for a sofa cushion, but Auntie will not change anything that is old; so it must hang where it hangs.

Over by the window stand three tall oleander trees full of bright red blossoms, and on the wall hangs a little book rack which is just large enough to hold the prayer book, the New Testament, *The Love Life*, by Johan Michael Lindblad, and the thick book that Aunt Lovisa studied when she went to school at Åmål. All she needed to know of French, geography, Swedish history, nature study, and domestic economy was contained between the covers of this book.

We see Aunt Lovisa dash away a tear, but she goes on with her reading just the same. Sometimes Gerda rises from her stool and asks Auntie whether she should put black or white trimmings on her dollie's dress.

"Dear child, do as you like!" But after a little Auntie is sorry she spoke hastily, and tells Gerda what she wants to know.

I am wondering all the while what I should do so that God will let my papa live. I should like to ask Aunt Lovisa's advice about this, but I am too shy.

Before long the housekeeper comes in with a tray.

"Have a wee drop of coffee, Mamselle Lovisa," she says. "You need it when there's so much sadness here. Not that the Lieutenant is dying——"

"No, Maja, I can't drink any coffee today." Then, thinking it would be ungracious of her not to accept when the housekeeper had gone to the trouble of preparing the coffee, she lays the book aside and pours out a cup for herself.

As she does so I rush over to see what that thick book she is reading might be. All the other books in the house I am familiar with, but this one I have never seen before. It is a large, bulky volume with a stout binding of brown leather, warped and faded, and a brass clasp and mounting of brass. But the title is in such curious lettering I can scarcely decipher it.

"Oh, see!" the housekeeper exclaims—"the Paymaster of the Regiment's Bible! It's many a year since I've seen that Book, and I have wondered what had become of it."

"That Bible has been in the cupboard of my attic storeroom since the death of my mother," says Aunt Lovisa. "But today I decided to take it out."

"You did right, Mamselle Lovisa. The Paymaster

always declared that that Book was better than all
the doctors and all the medicines in the world."

"Aye, that Book was his solace in every need. Do
you remember, Maja, that Father used to say he had
read this Book from cover to cover at least fifty
times?"

"Yes, indeed, I remember it well," the housekeeper
answers. "And I remember, also, how peacefully we
went to sleep of a night when we knew that the Paymaster of the Regiment lay reading his Bible in here!
It seemed as if no harm could come to us."

When Auntie and the housekeeper said that Grandfather had read the whole Bible fifty times, I looked
up. "Does Maja think that God was pleased with
Grandfather for reading the Bible through so many
times?"

"You may be certain that He was, Selma."

On receiving this assurance, something extraordinary comes over me. It is not anything that I,
myself, have thought of; but rather as if someone
had whispered into my ear what God would have
me do in order that Papa may recover.

I hesitate at first—the Book is so dreadfully thick.
What if it contains only sermons and admonitions?
—Well, what matter, if it saves my papa's life? Fold-
ing my hands, I make a solemn vow to God that if
He spares my father's life I will read the Bible from
cover to cover, and not skip a single word.

I have no sooner made that vow than Mamma
comes to the door. She looks more hopeful now than
she looked last night.

"How good of you, Lovisa, to take charge of the
children!" Mamma, apparently, is not aware that we
have run away from our lessons. "I came to tell you
that Gustaf has taken a sudden turn for the better.
His fever has abated, and he is no longer delirious.
It may be some time, however, before he is out of
danger, but with God's help I think he will be spared
to us."

I don't think it was so hard for Grandfather to read
the Bible through fifty times as for me to read it only
once. Grandfather could sit down to read whenever
he wished. Grandmother furnished lights for him to
read by, so that he could lie down and read his Bible
evenings.

If I were to tell Mamma or Auntie that I had promised God to read the Bible through so that Papa
would get well, perhaps I too could have a light to
read by at night. But it wouldn't do for me to speak
of this to anyone. Once there was a princess who had
twelve brothers who were changed into wild swans,
and in order that they might become human again
she had to knit them each a shirt of stinging nettle
yarn. The nettles pricked her fingers and tore her

hands, but she dared not tell why she was doing it;
nor do I.

The doctors at the institute in Stockholm ordered
me to rest for an hour every day after dinner, and I
have done so here, too. This is what Papa always
made me do when I was little. So, during the rest
hour I read the Bible. Not for long, however, as
Mamma always comes to tell me I must close the
Book and go to sleep awhile.

Anyhow, I'm glad that Aunt Lovisa does not carry
the Bible up to her attic storeroom and lock it away
in her wardrobe. I think it was God Who ordered it
left on the shelf of the yellow corner cupboard above
the trapdoor to the cellar. That cupboard is never
locked, and I can take the Book as often as I wish.

Aunt Lovisa says it is well that I am reading the
Bible. For under the lid of her sewing basket she
always has a novel concealed, which she reads when
no one is looking. Once or twice I borrowed one of
these novels and forgot to return it. But now that I
am reading the Bible, her novels are not disturbed.
Mamma and Aline Laurell do not approve of my
reading indiscriminately. Once they took away from
me a book entitled *The Woman in White* just as I
had come to the most exciting part. But Mamma and
Aline have no objection to my reading the Bible; for
the Bible is the Word of God.

It is a good thing, too, that spring is here with its

white nights. On Sundays we don't have to rise before eight, and I can lie abed and read the Bible for several hours. But the Book is so long it seems as though I could never finish it.

Gerda sleeps in the bedroom belowstairs, but she always comes up to the nursery before she is half dressed, and wants to play at toss and catch with the pillows. She can't understand why I lie here reading and do not want to play. It makes her very sad. I am sorry, but it can't be helped. One has to endure harder things than this if one is to read the whole Bible at ten years of age.

I wonder at times if Grandfather read every word in the Bible, as I am doing. I read the genealogy and all the laws, and everything about the sacrificial rites and about the Tabernacle and the vestments of the High Priest. I also wonder if Grandfather could pronounce all the strange words, and if he understood everything he read.

I have read in the biblical history most of the things recorded in the Bible. I know all about Adam and Eve, the Flood, the Tower of Babel, and also about Abraham and Joseph and David; but I am reading it again, word for word, since that is what I promised God.

It is Sunday morning. Anna, Emma Laurell, Gerda, and I are out walking. It is the only thing we can do during the month of May. The winters are much jollier, for then we can go skating or sledding or drive the stable ram. Even April is better than May, for one can dig canals in the wet snow on the country road or dam up waterfalls in the brook. But in May there is nothing to do but gather wood anemones, which may be fun for a day or two; but we have already tired of that. Now we just walk along the road, having as dull a time of it as if we were grown folk.

Anna and Emma Laurell are walking on one side of the road, talking in low tones. Their talk is of boys and of pretty dresses. Such things they seem to think Gerda and I are too young to understand. We walk on the opposite side of the road, and I'm telling Gerda about a beautiful play I once saw at the Royal Dramatic Theatre in Stockholm, called *My Rose of the Forest.*

All of a sudden, Anna and Emma come over to our side. They, too, want to hear about the play. "It must have been wonderful," they exclaim. Emma Laurell then tells us that in Karlstad, when her father lived, she and her sisters used to dress up and do theatricals. And Anna says that perhaps we too might do them here some day.

"Why not today?" says Emma Laurell. "Uncle Lagerlöf is well enough to be up, and we have gone over our lessons for tomorrow."

We face about quickly and almost run home to

play *My Rose of the Forest*, talking and planning all the way. Before we reach the avenue most of the parts have been assigned. Emma Laurell is to play the young girl who is called "My Rose of the Forest," because she has pretty red cheeks. Anna is to play the young gentleman who is in love with her. She is pale and has dark hair, which is suitable for a lover. The Old Man of the Forest, with whom Emma Laurell lives, I'm going to play. For I have long white hair, just like the Old Man at the theatre. But where shall we find someone who can play the Old Man's housekeeper? Gerda won't do, as she is too small for the part. Finally we decide to make up with Nurse Maja—although she kept us waiting at the inn while she stood on the barn steps gabbling with Lars Nylund—and let her be the housekeeper.

Gerda is disappointed because she is to have no part to play, and begins to cry. We feel uneasy, for once Gerda starts crying she'll keep it up all day. The grown-ups might think we had been mean to her, and forbid us to play theatre. Therefore we tell Gerda that she may play a little brother to Emma Laurell and sit on a stool and dress her dollies. She is content with that, thank goodness!

When we come home we have to listen first to the reading of a sermon! But just as soon as it is over we tell Mamma that we are going to play theatre; and Mamma lets us have the key to the big closet in the garret. We hunt up all sorts of discarded clothing, which we try on. It's heaps of fun.

The nursery is our stage, and the scene is supposed to be a big forest in which there is a small cottage enclosed by a high wall. We can't have the forest or a cottage, but we must have the wall for Anna to jump over when she comes to court Emma Laurell.

So we build a wall of all the beds, bureaus, tables, and chairs in the nursery and cover it with blankets and quilts to make it look like a wall. For without that wall it would be impossible to do the play as it was done in Stockholm. It is awfully hard to make the wall stand; it keeps tumbling all the while. The actors, when not on the stage, will have to stand by to hold the wall up.

The audience is to sit out in the garret. No curtain will be necessary, as we have only to open the door of the nursery for the spectators to have the whole stage before them. Inside the wall we have placed a table, a chair, and a stool on which Gerda is to sit. We hope everyone will understand that the table, the chair, and the stool represent the cottage where My Rose of the Forest lives with her grandfather. We rehearse the play once. I tell Anna and Emma Laurell the lines they are to speak. Emma Laurell can hardly keep from laughing, and I fear she will ruin the play; but Anna is excellent.

As we are about to begin the performance Uncle

Kalle Wallroth and Aunt Augusta arrive from Gårdsjö to see whether Papa is well enough to go with
them to Filipstad, to Aunt Julia's wedding. How
provoking! Now neither Mamma nor Aunt Lovisa
nor Aline Laurell can come to see our play! They will
have to entertain Auntie and Uncle. But when Auntie
and Uncle hear that a play is to be presented that
has been given at the Royal Dramatic Theatre in
Stockholm, they want to see it, too. Then Papa suddenly becomes interested. He puts on his fur coat
and escorts them up to the theatre.

It is too bad we must have Gerda on the stage
dressing her dolls when she doesn't belong in the
play! As soon as we open the door, ready to begin the
performance, Papa asks Gerda what part she is to
play, and Gerda answers as if she were herself and
not the small brother of My Rose of the Forest. And
Nurse Maja is no good, either; for she overdoes her
part. She has borrowed the housekeeper's big Paisley
shawl and carries a cane, with which she thumps the
floor as she walks, and she is all bent over, and grins
horribly, so that she looks like an old hag.

But Emma Laurell is charming; so is Anna. Anna
is wearing a military jacket that Papa had worn in
the days when he was a cadet in Stockholm. Her hair
is drawn up under a military cap, and we have
painted a black moustache on her. Emma is wearing

Mamma's white satin wedding dress and has her hair
hanging.

I have long, hanging locks, too, like the Old Man
at the Dramatic Theatre, and am wearing a short
jacket which Johan has outgrown, and the long
bloomers I wore at the institute. So I think the audience will know that I am the grandfather.

I'm so glad that Anna got over the wall without
knocking it down or stumbling, for the whole play
hinges on that.

Once, when I'm on the stage scolding Emma
Laurell for allowing Anna to scale the wall, I hear
laughter out in front and, looking round, I see Gerda
shaking her forefinger at a doll—mimicking me.
Never again will she be included in any of our theatricals!

Emma Laurell acts well, but she has a big smudge
on her upper lip where Anna kissed her. The rest of
us can scarcely keep from laughing. When the play
is over we receive more applause than the actors who
played the piece at the Dramatic Theatre.

Afterward, we have to put everything in order,
both in the nursery and in Mamma's attic closet; so
it is some time before we are through. When at last
we come downstairs Mamma says that Papa is tired
and has gone to bed, but he would like to have us
come to his room. And we go at once.

"Thank you, children," he says as we stand by his bedside. "I want to tell you that this has done me more good than all Dr. Piscator's pills."

And that, of course, is the best news we could have. Then we go into the parlour to pay our respects to Uncle Kalle and Aunt Augusta. They, too, are pleased with our performance and say they have had such a good time.

We begin to think we are wonderful. Uncle Kalle pats me on the head and chucks me under the chin. "So this is the girl who directed the play," he says in his usual jovial voice. I expect him to praise me and say it was awfully clever of me to coach the others in a play produced at the Royal Dramatic Theatre in Stockholm. But instead he says, in sepulchral tones, "But are you not supposed to be a little pietist who carries a big Bible around with her everywhere?"

I feel too embarrassed for words, but I can't tell him why I'm reading the Bible. Uncle, seeing how disappointed I am, pats me on the cheek as he adds, "Auntie and I haven't laughed so heartily in many a day. The next time you come to Gårdsjö you must give that play there."

I understand that Uncle Kalle wants to comfort me, but just the same I'm dreadfully uneasy. What if Papa should hear that people are calling me a pietist?

There is so much to be endured if one reads the whole Bible when one is only ten years old!

Aline Laurell has borrowed a novel from Fru Unger of West Ämtervik which is said to be very entertaining. She has lent it to Mamma and Aunt Lovisa; and they are so eager to see how the story ends they can hardly lay the book down.

I have seen the book both in Mamma's room and in Aunt Lovisa's. It is entitled *A Capricious Woman*, and is by Emilie Flygare-Carlén. How I should love to read it!

One Sunday morning the book lay on the dining-room table for several hours, and I could have read many chapters, but I did not open it. Until I have read the Bible through I will not begin another book.

It is a good thing, too, that summer is here. Aline and Emma Laurell have gone home to Karlstad. As we have no lessons now, I can read the Bible for several hours every day. But the summer is also troublesome, for Daniel and Johan are at home from school. And of course they have been told that I'm reading the Bible, and are forever teasing me about it.

"Listen, Selma," they say. "You who read the Bible, do you know where Jacob went when he was in his fourteenth year?" Or, "Do you know, Selma, what the twelve apostles are doing in the Kingdom

of Heaven?" Or, "Can you tell us who was the father
of Zebedee's children?"

But what does it matter? You have to put up
with more than that if you read the whole Bible
when you're only ten.

Papa is up and dressed, but he lies on the sofa
two or three hours every day. He feels tired and
weak, and his cough still hangs on. He says he may
never be himself again.

Papa, Mamma, and Anna have been to Filipstad
to Aunt Julia's wedding; but the journey didn't do
Papa any good, and now Mamma thinks he should
go to Strömstad for the summer, and take the baths
for the sake of his health. But I know that it is not
necessary. He will get well anyhow as soon as I've
finished the Bible; but I can't tell this to anyone.

Perhaps God has made it possible for Papa to go
away so that I may continue the reading.

So long as Papa is not himself we don't tell him
anything that might upset him. Therefore no one
at home has told him that people think I was converted by Paulus of Sandarne when I heard him
preach at the inn, and that I am now a pietist.

But maybe he'll hear of it anyhow. What shall I
say if Papa asks me why I am reading the Bible?
It won't do to lie about it, and it won't do to tell him
the truth.

It is well, at all events, that the summer nights are

long and light. As soon as Mamma has heard our prayers and Anna has gone to sleep, I crawl out of bed and sit by the window, to read for hours and hours.

Papa has come back from Strömstad, hale and strong as he was before he went tax-collecting and slept between wet sheets. We are all so glad he is home again!

We have many guests in the house just now—oh, so many! Uncle Schenson and Cousins Ernst and Klaës and Alma are here, and Uncle Hammargren and Aunt Nana with Teodor, Otto, and Hugo. Then, too, we have Uncle Oriel Afzelius and Aunt Georgina with their children, Elin and Allan, besides our bachelor uncle, Kristofer Wallroth.

Aline and Emma Laurell have also come, not to start school, however, but to be here on the seventeenth of August, when Papa will be fifty years old.

It is glorious weather, and the fruit this year is abundant. The gooseberries and currants are ripe; so are the cherries, and the greenings are almost ready to pick.

What a pity I have not finished the Bible yet! I'm reading the Book of Revelation now, so I'm almost at the end. But with so many guests in the house there's not a corner where I can sit down to read for an hour in comfort and peace while I finish the Book.

But, fortunately, Mamma has suggested that they

all go up to Storsnipan this afternoon to see the beautiful view. When both children and grown-ups have gone and I am alone in the house, I run into the kitchen bedroom and take the Bible out of the corner cupboard. Then, hurrying out to the garden, I seat myself under a gooseberry bush where I can eat gooseberries while reading the Book of Revelation. I'm so glad the Book is nearly finished and I won't have to keep any more secret vows.

In the midst of my reading I hear footsteps approaching, and, glancing up, whom should I see but Uncle Kristofer! And I thought he had gone with the others to Storsnipan! When he sees me sitting under a gooseberry bush with Grandfather's big Bible in my lap, he comes straight over to me. I tremble with fear when he asks me what I am reading; but I tell him, of course, that I am reading the Bible. And then he wants to know how much of the Book I have read, and I tell him that I have read it all but the last few chapters of the Book of Revelation, which I am reading now. He makes no comment, but from the look on his face I know that he is ready to burst out laughing.

When he has gone I close the Bible and carry it back to the kitchen bedroom and replace it on the shelf of the corner cupboard. I know well enough that when Papa and Uncle Schenson and Uncle Hammargren and Uncle Oriel return from Storsnipan,

Uncle Kristofer is going to tell them that he found me seated under a gooseberry bush reading the Book of Revelation. And when Uncle Kristofer relates anything he makes it so screamingly funny that the listeners laugh themselves sick.

I rush into the kitchen to help Aunt Lovisa and the housekeeper prepare supper. I run out to the kitchen garden and gather parsley and dill; and into the pantry for onions and pepper. In fact, I run all possible errands so as not to be seen when they come, or to hear Uncle Kristofer tell them how amused he was to find me sitting under a gooseberry bush reading the Book of Revelation.

There is much to do when the house is full of guests, and after supper I help with the dishes so that I may stay in the kitchen until my bedtime.

When we have many guests we children do not sleep in the nursery. Aunt Nana, Aunt Georgina, and Aline Laurell occupy it now. Anna, Emma Laurell, and Alma Schenson have to content themselves with a big clothes closet in the garret, while I sleep on the sofa in Mamma's and Papa's room.

Sometime in the night I am awakened by hearing my name—Mamma and Papa are talking about me.

"Did you hear what Kristofer said about Selma?" Papa asks—not as if he were angry but only amazed.

"Yes," says Mamma; "and I think he might have let the child alone."

"I've been away all summer, but you must have noticed whether she reads the Bible habitually."

"She has been reading the Book the whole summer, both early and late."

"But, my dear Louise, don't you think you should have forbidden her? Anyhow, that is no reading for a child."

"No, of course not," Mamma replies, "but Aline and I thought it best to leave her in peace."

"Then I shall have to talk to her myself," says Papa. "I don't want her to become an evangelist."

"No, Gustaf, you mustn't."

"But I don't understand——"

"Well, you see, I think she is reading the whole Bible in the hope that you may be restored to health."

"Oh, it isn't possible," says Papa.

"But you know how unhappy she was when you were stricken. She took it harder than any of the others, and ever since she has been diligently reading the Bible."

"Oh, it isn't possible," Papa says again. He clears his throat several times, as if it were hard for him to get the words across his lips. "It isn't possible that the girl is so simple-minded."

Mamma makes no answer, and Papa says nothing further.

I know that I may read the Bible as much as I

like, since Mamma stands up for me. But I never take down the Book from the shelf to finish the few pages in Revelation which I have not read.

For now that the mystery has been revealed, there is no power in the thing I vowed. It would be useless, therefore, to go on with the reading. So, what was the good of it all?

IV
GÅRDSJÖ

WE LOVE to go to Gårdsjö to visit Uncle Kalle
and Aunt Augusta, and to see our cousins Hilda and
Emilia and Karl and August and Elin and Julia and
Hugo! Gårdsjö is such a lovely place. The manor house
there is painted white and has an upper story and a
slate roof. Our house at Mårbacka is red, and has
only one story and just a tile roof. We have no grand
salon to dance in when we give parties, as they have
at Gårdsjö. They have a lake, too, at Gårdsjö, and
boats. We go rowing when we are there, and gather
water lilies. We love to row out among the reeds to
a round open space where no one can see us, and
where the reeds grow so tall that everything looks
green—the water, the skiff, the oars, and even we,
ourselves. We lie there perfectly still, and watch—
and at last a mother duck comes swimming past,

followed by a long line of little ducklings. It is all so mysterious and solemn! What a pity we have no lake at Mårbacka where we can go rowing! We have only a small duck pond.

At Gårdsjö they have also a river spanned by a bridge, on which we can stand and fish. As soon as we come to Gårdsjö we borrow fishing rods and go out on the bridge to angle for perch. Sometimes when we get a nibble we pull up only a small roach or a ruff; but we are delighted when we catch a perch, for the perch is a fish worth frying. But the roach is so full of bones that no one cares to eat it. Still, if we catch a roach now and then, it's nothing to be ashamed of. We are glad that it is not a ruff; for the ruff, like the slom, isn't fit to give to a cat. Wouldn't it be great if we had a river like this one to fish in at home! Our river in summer is only a shallow, muddy creek, and besides, it is a long way from the house. We never try to fish in that river.

There are so many interesting things to see at Gårdsjö, we scarcely have time for them all. They have a foundry there with a smelting furnace and a millrace. They also have a flour mill, a brickyard, and a sawmill. We have nothing of the kind at Mårbacka. We have only a little smithy where Per of Berlin mends sledges and wagon wheels, and an old handmill in which we grind salt when there is a big slaughter. When Papa built the barn he took up clay from the bottom of the pond; but that is not done any more. Lars of London and Magnus of Vienna saw wood in the stable yard, and to look at them is no pleasure.

Down by the iron works at Gårdsjö all the roads are black with coal dust; but they are smoother and much easier to walk on than gravelled roads. Before going into the works, we stop to look down at the millrace. It is so dark and threatening lying there, among the towering trees. A millhand once threw himself into the millrace because he couldn't have the miller's daughter. It seems strange that we should be standing on the very spot from which a man leaped to his death! No one has ever tried to drown himself in the duck pond at Mårbacka. The pond is so shallow it wouldn't be worth while to attempt it.

We don't care to go into the flour mill, for the air inside is thick with whirling flour dust. We would rather go into the smelting works.

The smeltery is large and awfully dark; the only light is that which comes through the half-round opening at the back of the furnace. There are no windows or plank flooring and no ceiling—only the tile roofing. Some of the tiles are broken; others have been blown away—which is fortunate, for otherwise we could not see where we were going.

In the middle of the smeltery is a big square hole filled with damp coal. To fall into that hole would

be the worst thing that could happen—above all, if
you were wearing your Sunday best. You have to walk
carefully when you're in the smeltery, for if you happened to step on a hot bar of iron you would burn
the soles off your shoes.

The old foundry at Gårdsjö is gloomy as a church
before the service begins. Old man Sternberg and
another smith are seated on a narrow wooden bench
at either side of the open furnace. All they have on is
a long shirt, wooden shoes, and a pair of goggles.
But we children regard them with awe, for they look
so serious and solemn. We dare not speak above a
whisper lest we should disturb them and they should
turn us out.

Sometimes Sternberg and sometimes the other
smith rises, goes over to the furnace, thrusts in an
iron bar, with which he bends and twists something
heavy and solid. At that sparks fly out of the furnace,
and the smith has to jump back quickly. Sometimes
a hot coal drops on his foot, and he has to kick off his
wooden shoes in a hurry. Every now and then the
fire boy comes with his wheelbarrow and scoops wet
coal from the dangerous hole and shovels it into the
furnace. Nothing more happens for a long, long time.
We grow tired of standing there waiting; but we
would not leave for anything.

At last both smiths rise and, grasping their crow-
bars, begin to poke in the furnace. They bend, pull,

and twist, the sweat pouring from them. Presently something red that sparkles and glows and is soft as dough rolls out. The two smiths then seize it with their tongs, drag it from the furnace over the floor, and lift it onto the anvil.

With that, it seems the heaviest work is done, and old man Sternberg looks pleased. His companion then pulls on a rope, and the huge trip hammer descends. To watch the hammer come down upon the hot metal on the anvil, striking sparks with every blow, is the grandest sight I have ever beheld! The hammer rises and falls, with a deafening noise. The water wheel, as it turns, forms a wreath of white foam, and all over the foundry comes a shower of flying red sparks. It is indeed a beautiful spectacle!

It is fun to go to the brickyard, too, for there we get clay cuckoos, and receive lumps of clay from which we mould plates and bowls. And it is just as much fun to go to the sawmill; but it lies too far away for me to walk.

We children are not sorry that the house at Gårdsjö is white and has an upper story and a slate roof. Indeed we are glad they have a lake and a river at Gårdsjö, and boats and fishing tackle and a mill dam and iron works and a brickyard and flour mill and sawmill and much else that is not to be found at Mårbacka. For so long as it is Uncle Kalle who lives there, we can come to Gårdsjö almost every Sunday; so we feel we have a part in all that's there.

When I grow up, I want to live in a house that is painted white and has an upper story and a slate roof; and I would like to have a grand salon where we can dance when we have parties.

V

HERRESTAD

AND WE children love to go to Herrestad, too, and visit with Uncle Noreen and Aunt Emilie and Cousins Adolf and Hedwig, Arvid and Erika and Emilia. Although the Noreens are not really related to us, they are cousins of our cousins at Gårdsjö, which is almost the same thing.

We think Herrestad is just as beautiful as Gårdsjö. There the manor house is also painted white and has an upper story and a slate roof and a grand salon for musicales and dancing. But they have no foundry at Herrestad; for, like Mårbacka, it is only a private estate. Herrestad is beautifully situated on the shore of Lake Fryken. Fryken is a big lake—so big that it stands both in the geography and on the map. The lake is over fifty miles long, and in the days when it could talk, it used to say: "Measure my length and you'll know my depth." So Fryken is a real lake.

There is a large evergreen park at Herrestad where
we love to walk. The paths have a thick carpet of
pine needles where we can slide as on ice. And there
are also huge rocks in the park down which we slide
sitting on a spruce bough.

Uncle Noreen has built a pavilion in the park, and
in that pavilion there are real windows and wallpaper.
The floor is of polished wood—short, narrow boards,
laid crisscross, that go up and down like waves. We
don't like to dance there because it makes us dizzy.
Uncle Noreen wrote a poem which he read at the
dedication; for he can write verse or make a speech
or play Erik XIV.

It is awfully funny to see Emilia Noreen, the
youngest child at Herrestad, act Erik XIV. She runs
round and round in circles shaking her tousled head
(for she is supposed to act insane, of course). "The
forest is calling my name," she says. "The forest is
calling my name! But does it know who I am?" And
she speaks in hollow tones. We are supposed to be
frightened; but she is such a sweet little thing that
we only laugh. Uncle Noreen, himself, has taught
her the part of Erik XIV, for he plays with his
children just as our papa does.

There is a deep rock cave in the park, called the
Bear's Grotto, because a bear once tumbled into it
and could not climb out again. We usually sit down
under a tall spruce at the edge of the grotto and

pretend the bear is still at the bottom of the cave. We hear him growl as he clambers up and hear the scraping of his claws against the wall as he tumbles back.

Wild blackberries grow at Herrestad and, strangely enough, are not to be found anywhere else in the parish. I think the bear was out hunting for blackberries when he fell into the grotto; for they are very good, and plentiful, too, around here.

I love Herrestad because so many strange things have happened here. Once upon a time an old countess lived here who never dared step outside the house because she feared the crows would eat her up. And then there was a young bride who was so unhappy that she would sit for hours on the shore of the lake, thinking of drowning herself. There is a room here they call the Blue Cabinet, where a young girl sat by the window one day and saw her lover drown in the Fryken. Sometimes I stand by that window, and then I always see the lake covered with ice and a young man coming on skates, when, suddenly, before him appears a wide crack in the ice—I quickly turn away, for I do not want to see any more.

A group of gentlemen were seated on the porch at Mårbacka one day discussing the relative merits of Gårdsjö and Herrestad. They were Uncle Schenson, Engineer Warberg, Pastor Unger, and Papa, of course. One of them declared that Herrestad was the finest place in the parish. Another said Gårdsjö was the finest. Papa listened awhile in silence, and presently he asked them if they had not forgotten to mention Mårbacka. Perhaps that place, all things considered, was just as good as either of the others.

The guests looked slightly embarrassed. Uncle Schenson then observed:

"True, Brother Erik Gustaf, you have put a lot of money and labor on Mårbacka and extended it considerably, and you manage your property remarkably well; still, you can't compare——"

"Yes, I know," Papa interrupted, "that Gårdsjö is a manufacturing estate and that Herrestad is the show place of the Fryken valley. But can you tell me why it is that Gårdsjö and Herrestad are continually changing owners? They have been bought and sold many times within my memory, while Mårbacka has passed from generation to generation as a heritage from the time the first settler took up his abode here."

"Well, there may be something in what you say, Erik Gustaf," Uncle Schenson conceded, "if, for instance, one only considers the homeliness and comfort of the place."

VI
FEAR

WE ARE having such a good time! Papa, Mamma, Aunt Lovisa, Aline Laurell, and Anna have gone to a party at the Sunne Deanery, and left Emma Laurell, Gerda, and me at home. They thought we were too young to go with them.

After learning our lessons we go out to the kitchen and ask the housekeeper to recite the funny jingles about Cockalittle who fretted himself to a shadow, and the old man who ate seven cartloads of porridge and drank seven cartloads of buttermilk. Then we persuade the nice scullerymaid to sing us the comic song about Olle Bock who went to the war with fifteen thousand men and promised to be back by Easter or by Holy Trinity. Afterward we roast apples in the tile stove in the dining room; and for supper cook gives us pancakes with raspberry jam

so we won't grieve because we have had to stay at
home.

As soon as we finish supper we hurry upstairs
to the nursery, for we feel lost in the big rooms
below with all the grown folks away. Gerda is to
sleep tonight on the sofa in the nursery. We can't
expect her to stay all alone in Mamma's and Papa's
room, so she and Nurse Maja come up with us. The
tall, red-haired girl, who helps with the work, and
the nice scullerymaid come, too—but only to talk,
for they have nothing to do with the nursery.

Nurse Maja freshens the fire and we gather around
it to warm ourselves. It has been raining in torrents
the whole evening. We sit in silence awhile and listen
to the beating of the rain against the window; to the
howling of the wind as it sweeps round the corner of
the house. The nice scullerymaid says it's too bad
that the family have to drive home on a night like
this. But Nurse Maja assures her that they are riding
in the big covered carriage. We all feel thankful to
hear that they are sheltered from wind and rain.

Then we beg the nice scullerymaid and the tall
helper to tell us some ghost stories. But they shake
their heads. They dare not, they say, for Fru Lagerlöf
has strictly forbidden them to tell ghost stories to the
children.

But Nurse Maja winks at us, as much as to say:
"Never mind, children; I'll find a way to get round

it, but first I must undress Gerda and put her to bed." Gerda falls asleep the moment her head touches the pillow, and Nurse Maja comes back to us.

We two, Emma Laurell and I, Nurse Maja says, are almost as sensible as grown folks, so it can't do us any harm to hear ghost stories. But as Gerda is only a child, Fru Lagerlöf doesn't want her to hear any harrowing tales.

We listen to one ghost story after another. The tall, red-haired helper tells us that in the last place where she was in service the master of the house died. He had not been a very good man. She didn't know just what was wrong with him, but the day he died a big black dog with a fiery red gape came running toward the house. The dog stood on the porch fully an hour, barking and howling to be let in, but no one dared open the door to him. It was the noon hour, and the menservants had come into the kitchen to eat dinner, but they sat at the table without touching their food.

She remembered that a large dish of potatoes had been placed before them and that one of the men had helped himself to a potato and ·sat holding it in his hand, but did not peel it. The red-haired helper was in the kitchen with the other servants, and she never could forget how uncanny it was as they all sat there in deathlike silence listening to the howling of the dog.

The mistress of the house came into the kitchen looking white as a ghost, her knees shaking with fright. She had to cling to the doorpost to keep from falling. She wanted to know if there was not someone in the house who dared drive that dog away.

The oldest of the menservants arose and pushed back his chair with a force that sent it crashing against the wall; he ran over to the fireplace and, seizing the tongs, snatched a burning brand from the hearth, and, quickly unbolting the door, opened it a trifle and threw the burning brand right into the open jaws of the howling demon who stood outside. At that, the dog let out a fiendish howl that could be heard far and wide. It sounded as if a man in a rage were cursing at the top of his lungs. As the demon ran down the avenue, clouds of smoke and sparks of fire flew around him; so the tall helper could not see what he was.

Without knowing it, I was clinging tight to Nurse Maja's hand. "Why, Selma, you're not scared, are you?" Maja asks, bending over me.

Although the cold chills ran up and down my back the whole time the red-haired girl had been talking, just the same it was terribly exciting. I drop Nurse Maja's hand and shake my head.

I wish they would tell stories of giants and elves and trolls, for of such I have no fear. If they would only stop talking of the Evil One! For, you see, I've always had a faint suspicion that the Evil One lurks in a dark corner of the garret, outside the nursery— the corner where the discarded spinning wheels and looms are stored. I always hurry by the place where I fancy he's hiding and might suddenly appear. As soon as I open the door of the nursery I feel safe; for he never comes in there. But maybe he will come now, since the tall, red-haired helper has talked so much about him! Who knows? Perhaps in a moment he may rap on the door, open it, and walk in!

It is the nice scullerymaid's turn now to tell a story. She begins by saying that she was not there when it happened; but just the same she knows it is true because an uncle of hers saw and heard it all.

Our scullerymaid's uncle was out in the forest one day cutting timber. He had a comrade—a fellow who was supposed to have some kind of agreement with Old Nick himself. They had just sawed through a spruce trunk and stood waiting for the tree to fall, when they noticed that it did not lean in the direction they expected. It looked as if the tree would crash down upon them before they had time to get out of its way.

And then our scullerymaid's uncle heard his companion shout to the big spruce: "In Satan's name, straighten!" At the command her uncle saw the tree stop in the middle of its fall, then rise, and come down on the opposite side.

I know it is stupid of me to be so frightened; but while the scullerymaid is narrating I hear footsteps out in the garret, and just as the tree comes crashing down, I cry out, "Stop!" Weeping, I spring to my feet and again tell her to stop. "I don't want to hear any more," I say.

"Why, Selma, it was only a tilepan that blew off the roof," says Nurse Maja. "But we'll stop now, since you are afraid."

I understand at last that Nurse Maja is right; it was nothing but a tilepan. I am so ashamed I could die. Emma Laurell says I behave like a child of six. She thinks the nice scullerymaid should be allowed to continue her story, but Nurse Maja says, "No! We have heard enough for tonight."

Afterward, I lie awake all night, worrying because I allowed myself to be scared. For I know well enough that the Evil One does not lurk among the old spinning wheels. That was only imagination. It was disgraceful of me to be frightened over nothing at all, and to cry because a tilepan fell off the roof. It shall not happen again.

I know a little girl who is on hand next day when dinner is being prepared, and who, if the housekeeper wants something that is in the storeroom, promptly offers to fetch it. She mounts the stairs and resolutely walks across the garret to the storeroom, with a firm and steady tread; and she does this day after day.

The housekeeper praises her for being so good as to run errands. But the girl does it only to harden herself. She will soon be able to pass the corner in the garret where the spinning wheels are, without having to avert her eyes or having that unpleasant thumping of the heart when she goes down to the kitchen again.

VII
THE CARD GAME

DURING the Christmas holidays, when Daniel and Johan are at home and Uncle Wachenfeldt is here, they play cards in the evening with Aunt Lovisa. They play a game called preference, but which they call priffe. I have learned the game by watching the others play. Usually it is only grown folks who play priffe. Neither Anna nor Emma Laurell can play that game. They know only such simple games as Snip-snap-snorum, Black Peter, Starve the Fox, Knave and Fool, and Dunderpart.

Papa has gone on a journey tonight and taken Johan with him. Daniel and Uncle Wachenfeldt don't see how they can have their usual game with the fourth man missing. They ask Mamma to join them; but she declines, as she does not care for card games. Then Aunt Lovisa suggests that they take Selma for the fourth man.

"But she can't play priffe," Uncle Wachenfeldt declares; "the child is only twelve years old!"

"You might try her, Wachenfeldt," says Aunt Lovisa; "she is not so bad at the game. She has played with us a number of times when Aline, Fru Lindegren, and I have indulged in a game of priffe."

So I am permitted to be the "fourth man" and have taken my place at the card table. It's great fun, especially with Daniel as my partner. He is always good-natured, whether he wins or loses, and says such funny things to make you laugh. Aunt Lovisa sits thumbing the cards a long while, but as soon as she lays a card on the table she regrets it and wants to take it back. Uncle Wachenfeldt, however, knows what card to play, for he has been a great gambler in his day. But now he has a cataract on one eye and does not see very well with the other; so he happens at times to throw down the wrong card. I become impatient when the others play badly, but Daniel never loses his temper no matter how they play.

I have good luck with the cards at first, but later on I get such poor hands that I lose and lose all the time. We do not play for money, but just the same it's provoking; for Daniel and Uncle Wachenfeldt may think their poor luck is due to their letting a child play with them.

Then at last, when it's near the supper hour and almost time to stop playing, I have a good hand. I hold the ace of spades, the king, queen, jack, and the ten-spot, also five low cards. There are ten sure points if I can only get them in. Besides, I have the ace of diamonds, and queen of hearts and a low in hearts, but no clubs.

Since I have had to say "pass" the whole evening, I want to take a turn at winning and show them what I can do. I can say "priffe" myself now, for with these cards I can take at least seven tricks. Opposite me sits Daniel, at my right Aunt Lovisa, and at my left Uncle Wachenfeldt—the two are playing against Daniel and me.

As I have said "priffe," it is Aunt Lovisa's lead. Auntie fingers the cards a moment and finally decides to play a club. Uncle Wachenfeldt happens to have good clubs, too; so he and Aunt Lovisa take five tricks with their clubs, while I have to throw away my good spades.

I feel so nervous now that I have to hide the hand that holds the cards under the table so no one will see how it trembles. When they have played all their clubs, Uncle Wachenfeldt throws down a heart; Aunt Lovisa follows with the ace, and I play my low heart. Auntie chuckles as she sweeps in the cards.

"This is going well for us, Wachenfeldt," she says.

But Daniel, who is generally so amiable, asks me rather sharply upon what I "priffed."

Now Aunt Lovisa plays the jack of hearts, and I cover it with my queen. This time Uncle Wachenfeldt does not take my queen, but plays a low card; so it looks as if the game would be mine. I think, "Ah! now I am saved." At last I can play my spades and my ace of diamonds, and make my seven points.

But before Daniel lays down his card he asks, turning to Uncle Wachenfeldt, "Why don't you take Selma's queen with your king?"

Uncle Wachenfeldt raises the cards to his eyes and squints at them through his big goggles. "Yes, my dear lad, I see that I have the king, but a card once played cannot be taken back."

"But you have a right to take it back," says Daniel, "as you could not see what you were doing."

I know that Daniel is right in saying that Uncle may take back his card; but I would like so much to win this game that I cannot agree with Daniel. "Didn't you hear Uncle say that a card once played is played?"

But Daniel doesn't care. "Play your king, Uncle," he says and hands him back the low card. Uncle Wachenfeldt then plays his king, and Daniel follows with a low in hearts; and the game goes to our opponents. Now that they have made their seven points, there is no possible chance of my taking a single trick. When Aunt Lovisa puts out her hand and gathers up the four hearts my patience is at an end. Rising, I throw all my cards on the table.

"I won't play with you any longer," I shout, "for you don't play fair!"

I'm so angry that my blood fairly boils. I think Uncle Wachenfeldt is a contemptible wretch, a regular card sharp. It does me good to be able to throw my cards on the table and tell him so to his face. And Daniel is not a bit better. They are not the sort a decent person can play cards with.

It is something unheard of at Mårbacka for one to throw his cards on the table and accuse the other players of cheating; so, naturally, it creates consternation. Mamma, who has been sitting all evening at another table with Anna and Gerda, rises at once and comes toward me. I run to her, shrieking, "Mamma, they don't play fair!" And, throwing my arms about her, I suddenly burst into tears.

Without either reprimanding or defending me, Mamma takes me firmly by the wrist and leads me out of the dining room. We pass through the hall and up the garret stairs into the nursery. All the while I'm shrieking hysterically: "They didn't play fair, Mamma; they didn't play fair!" But Mamma doesn't say a word.

When we have entered the nursery she lights the candle and turns down my bed. "Now undress your-

self and get into bed," she says quietly. But instead
of undressing, I fling myself into a chair, blubbering:
"Uncle Wachenfeldt didn't play fair."

As I say it again, a strange thing happens to my
eyes. Instead of looking out upon the nursery, they
turn in upon myself. And what they see is a deep,
dark, empty cavern with dank walls and marshlike
bottom of mud and slime.

As I sit peering in I see something move in the
slimy depths—something that tries to work its way
up. Suddenly a huge head appears above the surface,
a hideous, crested head with gaping jaws, and I
catch a glimpse of a dark scaly body, with short,
thick forelegs and long, sharp claws. It is like the
dragon Saint George battles with at Storkyrkan in
Stockholm, only larger and more terrifying.

I have never seen anything so dreadful as this
monster that lives in me. The mere thought of it
frightens me almost to death! Until now it must
have been sleeping at the bottom of the slime, for
when I flew into a rage the monster awoke. I must
hurry before the whole long beast is out of the mire,
or perhaps it can never be forced back again.

I jump to my feet and begin to undress. I have
stopped crying, but I am still terribly afraid of the
thing which my eyes have beheld. I creep into bed,
and when Mamma has tucked me in I take her hand
and kiss it.

Then Mamma sits down on the edge of my bed. She knows that I'm not angry now. Perhaps she also knows that I am afraid of myself, for Mamma knows everything.

"In the morning you will beg Uncle Wachenfeldt's pardon," she says.

"Yes," I answer.

Mamma says nothing more, but she still sits on the edge of my bed. I lie thinking of the hideous monster that lives within, and I say to myself that never again will I give way to anger. That beast must lie at the bottom of its slimy cave as long as I live. It shall not be allowed to raise its ugly head again.

I don't know what Mamma is thinking; she ought to warn me but she doesn't. But as she understands everything, perhaps she knows that it isn't necessary. After a little she asks me if I would not like something to eat.

"No," I reply.

"Then say your prayers. I'll sit here afterward until you fall asleep."

VIII
THE MARSEILLAISE

IF ONLY Uncle Kristofer had not come upon me when I sat under the gooseberry bush reading the Book of Revelation, and if he had not told Papa about it, and if Papa had not taken Mamma to task, he would have been well by this time. But since he found out everything before I had time to finish the Book, I fear there is no help for him.

In summer he feels fairly well; but as soon as cold weather sets in his cough returns. Although he rubs his chest with mutton tallow every night and sleeps with the stocking wound round his neck that he has worn on his left foot during the day, the cough still hangs on.

Mamma continually begs him to send for Dr. Piscator, but Papa says he would rather not call Dr. Piscator, for he is one of those perpetual "undergrads" who has spent most of his life at Upsala

University, where he acquired the habit of sitting up all night, talking and drinking toddy. One can't get rid of him before two or three in the morning.

So instead Papa tries to doctor himself. He has given up his daily walks along the country road because if he meets people he has to stop and chat; and in that way he catches more cold. Mamma thinks there's no need of his stopping to talk; he could just as well bow in passing. But that would be impossible for him.

Papa wants porridge for supper every night, and he won't come with us now when we're invited out to supper because he can't have his porridge at these "strange" places. Mamma could barely persuade him to go with us to the Deanery, to call on Professor Fryxell. Why, he wouldn't even go to Gårdsjö until Aunt Augusta hit upon the idea of having her cook make porridge for him. Nor is he pleased when we have guests to supper at home. Aunt Lovisa thinks it most embarrassing that he should eat nothing but porridge for supper, and at times pretends she has forgotten it. But Papa declares he will never get well unless he can have his porridge. So Aunt Lovisa is obliged to bring him in a dish, no matter how many fine guests we have at table.

Papa also thinks that he must take a "bracer" before breakfast and two before dinner. He says that corn brandy is the best of all remedies, and if he only takes this medicine long enough he'll be restored to perfect health. He is positive that this is a sure cure. Papa had never tasted brandy before his illness, but when he had the ague Grandmother cured it by giving him brandy. Both Mamma and Aunt Lovisa tell him that, judging from what they have seen, people are also harmed by drinking brandy; but Papa says they are all wrong, for isn't he getting better every day?

But we children know that Papa is failing because he doesn't romp with us any more. He has been doctoring himself nearly two winters, yet his cough is no better. He gets no rest from it day or night.

Mamma wants to send for Dr. Piscator at once, but Papa protests. For now that Germany and France are at war it would be more dangerous than ever to call in Dr. Piscator. You see, the doctor sides with the Germans against all of us. He thinks they are a great people, and is forever singing their praises. We have been told that once when the Nilssons of Visteberg sent for him, he and Herr Nilsson got into a heated argument over Germany and France, which lasted all night. Fru Nilsson had to give him his breakfast before he departed. So Papa is right—it would be foolhardy to send for Dr. Piscator.

In the end, however, Mamma has her way. The doctor is called one afternoon. He arrives a little before four; so we think that when he has examined

Papa and prescribed for him, and has had his afternoon coffee, he will surely go.

But he lingers over the coffee cups, and talks and talks. When the clock points to five, Papa orders hot water, sugar, and cognac brought to his room, so that the doctor can have his toddy. "The chances are he'll not leave before he has had his grog," thinks Papa.

The weather had been moderate all day, but toward evening it grew bitterly cold, and by half-past five the thermometer had dropped to twenty degrees below zero.

We are sitting, as usual, at the round table in the dining room, crocheting, embroidering, and sewing, but when the penetrating cold begins to creep along the floor our feet become like clumps of ice. We pity the stableman, who must drive the doctor back to Sunne on a night like this.

At six o'clock Aunt Lovisa begins to wonder if the doctor is going to stay for supper, but Mamma and Aline Laurell think it unlikely. Why should he stay? Surely he who is a physician must have sense enough to know that his patient should retire early.

While we are talking, the housekeeper comes to tell us that there is the grandest display in the heavens which we ought to see. We quickly put on our wraps and run out.

The whole sky is red as if it were aflame. Aline

Laurell says it is the aurora borealis. We stand gazing in breathless wonder, for we have never seen anything so marvelous. High in the heavens rise tier upon tier of fiery red organ pipes, and all at once there sweep across the sky clouds of blue and green, and as they move we seem to hear a hissing sound.

Someone remarks that this must be a reflection from the siege of Paris, which is now taking place. But Aline Laurell says that that is impossible. Still, it might be a sign that there is sorrow and wrath in heaven because the wicked Germans are bombarding a great city like Paris. We think it is all so unspeakably cruel.

It is too cold to stand outside any longer. As we turn to go in, we feel as if grenades and bombs were bursting all about us; so we can understand what they must suffer in the great beleaguered city.

When we come in it is half-past six, and Aunt Lovisa asks again whether the doctor is going to stay for supper. She has a sausage lying in water, but is afraid it is a bit salty. There must be something relishing to put on the *smörgås* table in case he should stay. But Mamma feels quite sure that the doctor will leave before supper, as he has to send home Papa's medicine from the apothecary's in Sunne, which he couldn't do unless he went before bedtime.

At seven o'clock Papa comes into the dining room with the glad tidings that the doctor is ready to leave, and begs us to notify the stableman to hitch up at once. Anna runs out to the kitchen with the message, and we are all glad that Papa may at last have peace.

Before Papa goes back to his room, Mamma wants to know what he and the doctor have been talking about all this time.

"We talked only of Bismarck," Papa replies wearily, "and his colossal achievements."

We feel sorry for Papa, who has had to listen to eulogies of Bismarck, for of course we know that he is to blame for all the misfortunes which France is passing through. And we know what we are talking about, since we have been out and seen Paris bombarded.

The stableman isn't slow in hitching up! It is no time at all before we hear the sound of sleigh bells as he comes driving toward the house. The gentlemen in the bedroom must have heard it, too; but they go right on talking.

"Selma," says Mamma, "you go tell them the sleigh is waiting."

As I open the door to the bedroom I find Papa and the doctor seated at the writing table with the toddy tray between them. The doctor excitedly pounds on the table and shouts: "It was that damned Spanish hag——"

Seeing me, he breaks off long enough to hear what is wanted. When I have informed him that the sleigh is at the door, he says, with a wave of his hand, "All right," and turns again to Papa.

I go back to the dining room at once and tell them what the doctor has said. Aline Laurell becomes highly indignant.

"It is shameful of him to speak in that way of the poor Empress, who has been banished from her country."

We sit anxiously waiting for the doctor to go. The thermometer has now dropped to twenty-five below zero, and we fear for the servant and the horse. Mamma sends out a fur coat to the man and a blanket to spread over the horse.

"That is all I can do," she says with a sigh.

When it is going on half-past seven the stableman stamps across the hall and into the bedroom. What he says in there we cannot hear, but we understand that he wants to know how much longer he must wait. At all events, he is not there very long, before we hear his step again in the hall. This time he comes to the dining room.

"What do you think I should do, Frua? I am afraid the horse will freeze to death out there."

"What did the gentlemen say?"

"What did they say? Well, the Lieutenant couldn't get a word in edgewise, for as soon as I came in, the doctor poured me out a drink of cognac and gave me a two-skilling piece, then he drove me out."

"Did he?" says Mamma. "Well, Jansson, then you'd better unhitch the mare and lead her back to the stable."

The stableman has barely shut the hall door behind him when Papa comes into the dining room. "I don't think that the doctor will leave before he has had his supper," he says.

"He shall have his supper, of course," Mamma replies. "But I do hope he won't sit at the table all night!"

"I can't answer for that," says Papa. "But if worse comes to the worst, we can shoo him out."

Then Papa goes again to his room, and Aunt Lovisa mutters, as if to herself, that it will be the same here as it was at the Nilssons in Visteberg—we shall have him at breakfast, too.

"In that case," says Mamma, "Papa will be utterly exhausted, and I shall have him lying between sheets tomorrow."

Since it was Mamma who said that, we become greatly concerned. We are furious at Dr. Piscator for staying so long. And as we sit there in blank despondency, Aline Laurell suddenly bursts out laughing.

"I believe I can send the doctor home," she says, "if Fru Lagerlöf will permit me to try."

"To be sure you may try," says Mamma; "but you mustn't do anything to make him angry."

"I promise you I'll do nothing to offend him."
Aline quickly lays aside her needlework and rises.
Mamma and Aunt Lovisa, Anna, Emma, and Gerda
are blue with the cold, and look woebegone; but
Aline's cheeks are red as roses and her eyes sparkle
with mischief.

Formerly we had only a spinnet, but when Grandfather died, about two years ago, we fell heir to his
piano, which stands now in our parlour. Aline goes
into the parlour and opens the piano. She lights the
candles, then searches in the pile of sheet music until
she finds what she's looking for. Shortly after, she
strikes up a march.

We sit perfectly still and listen. We are so curious
that we can neither knit nor sew. "What is she playing?" says Aunt Lovisa, as if trying to recall something. "I seem to have heard that march before."

"It sounds familiar," says Mamma. "Why, I believe it is the Marseillaise!"

"Ah, so it is!" says Aunt Lovisa. "What a glorious
march! It's a pleasure to hear it again."

"They used to play it continually at Filipstad in
my youth," says Mamma. "I remember how pleased
Father was whenever he heard that march."

Mamma and Aunt Lovisa look quite animated, but
we children can't understand why.

"What is the Marseillaise?" asks Anna.

"It is a French march," Mamma explains—"the

one which was played and sung in France during the French Revolution. Listen! Isn't it inspiring?"

"I have never heard Aline play so well," Aunt Lovisa remarks. "But I wonder what Dr. Piscator will say to that music?"

Ah! Now I remember reading about the Marseillaise in Nösselt's *Popular History for Women*, or in some other book. I read that the French loved that song so much that just hearing it inspired them to great deeds of bravery. I listen with rapt attention as Aline plays the Marseillaise. She plays it over and over again.

I know not why it is, but the strains of that music have a magical effect. One cannot sit quietly knitting or sewing; one wants to jump up and sing and shout. It fills one with a burning desire to do something extraordinary—something big.

We have never before heard Aline Laurell play like that. We did not know there was so much sound in Grandfather's old piano. I fancy I can hear the drums; I can hear the shooting and the clash of arms. I seem to feel the earth tremble. I have never heard anything that stirs the imagination like that march!

The bedroom where Papa sits with Dr. Piscator is next to the parlour; so of course they must hear the Marseillaise. I can't help wondering if they, too, do not think it beautiful.

When Aline sat down at the piano it was exactly

eight o'clock; it is now a quarter past, but she plays on and on with the same verve and force.

There is something Aline wants to tell us who listen. I can hear it, but I cannot say exactly what it is. Perhaps it is this: "Do not disparage the French, for they are a great, a wonderful people." Or perhaps this is what it means: "You must not grieve because they have fallen, for they will rise again." It means something of the sort, I'm sure.

A moment later Papa appears at the door of the parlour.

"You may stop now, Aline, for Dr. Piscator has gone."

Papa then tells us how strangely the doctor acted when he heard the Marseillaise. At first he paid no attention to it and went on talking; but when the playing continued he swore a bit and said the noise disturbed him. Suddenly he stopped talking and listened. Then he began to hum the air, beating time with his feet, and Papa was almost certain that the doctor's eyes were moist.

All of a sudden he jumped up and walked toward the door, where his fur cap and coat were hanging; hastily drawing them on and pulling his cap down over his ears, he shouted: "Good-bye to you, Erik Gustaf! I'm going now!"

He opened the door and rushed out into the hall, with Papa hurrying after him. "But my dear fellow,"

Papa protested, "you can't go until the sleigh drives up. Come in again and sit down a few minutes while I send word to the servants' hall."

But the doctor was in a tearing hurry and quickly opened the front door. "Do you think I can't find the way to the servants' hall myself?" he said. "I won't stay here another minute. If I were to sit listening to the Marseillaise much longer I'd soon be as crazy about the French as the rest of you are."

IX
FORTY DEGREES BELOW ZERO

Today is Saturday, and as we have no school on Saturday afternoon, the weather being fine and the going good, Mamma thought it would be a pleasant change for Aunt Lovisa and Aline Laurell to drive to Gårdsjö, and, at the same time, get a few samples of cotton print which Aunt Augusta had promised her. They were not to stay so long that Aunt Augusta would feel obliged to invite them to supper, but were to leave for home as soon as they had had their afternoon coffee.

After they had gone, Papa sent for Anna and me to come to the office and check fire insurance papers—for Papa has charge of all the fire insurance in East Ämtervik. There are three policies for every house, and all three must be exactly alike.

We are sitting at the large writing desk in the office, with a huge pile of insurance papers before us. We feel very important in being able to help Papa with the checking.

Papa reads: "New I. Form I. Old Roof ½ Birchbark and Turf." The same thing is repeated without variation, in paper after paper. But we enjoy the work none the less. Papa calls Anna Inspector Nyman and me Erik of Korterud; for it is those two men who generally do the checking. If I find an error, he says: "That's right, Erik of Korterud, you show 'em up." It sounds so funny that we have to lean back in our chairs and laugh.

While we are laughing the loudest, the office door opens and in comes a man wearing a long black fur coat with a crocheted woollen travelling belt and a sealskin cap. His beard and eyebrows are so thick with frost that we don't recognize him at first, but we soon know him to be Engineer Frykberg from Gräsmark, who comes every seventeenth of August to dance and enjoy the festivities.

When he has shaken hands with Papa, Anna, and me, he says he has heard that Papa has a big crop of oats this year and that he would like to buy a little seed, for at Gräsmark the autumn frosts have destroyed all their oats.

Papa lays aside the insurance papers and sends us children over to the house to tell Mamma to invite Engineer Frykberg for coffee. As Aunt Lovisa is away, we children help the housekeeper crush sugar and fill the cake basket with rye rusks and small cakes. We think we have arranged the coffee tray very well. But when Engineer Frykberg comes into the dining room and casts a glance at the table, his face falls.

"Don't all your womenfolk drink coffee?" he says to Papa. "The table is laid only for three."

"Oh, yes," answers Papa. "That is a habit they have all acquired; but my sister and the governess have gone to Gårdsjö, so you'll have to be content with just us."

It seems strange that Engineer Frykberg, who is a man of powerful build with long black throat whiskers plentifully sprinkled with gray, should take it so hard because Aunt Lovisa and Aline Laurell have gone to Gårdsjö. He blinks his eyes rapidly several times, then takes out a large red bandanna and mops his face. When he holds out his cup so that Mamma can pour coffee for him, the spoon clinks against the saucer.

Mamma looks up, not in the least disturbed by Engineer Frykberg's singular behavior. She says with a smile:

"They are not going to stay at Gårdsjö the whole evening. I think they will be back by six o'clock."

When Mamma says that, Engineer Frykberg brightens up; he puts his handkerchief back into his pocket, and the spoon suddenly stops jingling against the saucer.

While they drink their coffee, Mamma talks to Engineer Frykberg about Aline Laurell. She is very fortunate, she says, in having such an excellent governess for her children, and one who is so orderly, so modest, and so pleasant to have in one's home. In addition, she has such capable hands! She can make the prettiest things out of nothing at all.

Mamma begs that the engineer will look at a couple of lambrequins we have in the dining room, which Aline gave Papa last Christmas. "Just see how beautifully these lambrequins are embroidered! Would you think that these roses and fuchsias and lilies-of-the-valley were made of nothing but fish scales? And this pretty border is made of pine cones which she has varnished. I tell you, that girl has a fortune in her hands."

Mamma bids me fetch Papa's pen rest to show to Engineer Frykberg. Aline made it out of a few thin pieces of wood, glued together. Papa likes it so well that he will have no other pen rest on his writing table. "So you see that this didn't cost us anything, either."

Then she shows him the fine bookshelves in the parlour which Aline made from three board ends hung on brown woollen cords. The shelves have a border of black velvet on which Aline has worked flowers and leaves of fish scales, white silk, and beads of straw. "This she gave me for Christmas, last year," says Mamma. "Don't you think it is pretty?"

"Yes." Although Engineer Frykberg admires everything Mamma shows him, he is not so enthusiastic as she had expected. He thinks it a great pity that so capable a girl as Aline should have to embroider with fish scales and spruce cones.

When he has finished his coffee he is seized with a new unrest. Time and again he fishes in his waistcoat pocket and pulls out his big silver watch, glances at it, puts it back, then pulls it out again, as if he had forgotten the time.

After Mamma has finished talking about Aline Laurell, Papa asks Engineer Frykberg to tell him something about the beautiful mountain they have up in Gräsmark, called Gettjärnsklätten. He asks him if it is true that a Finn boy, while tending a herd last summer, found a big nugget of gold, which he exchanged at the goldsmith's in Karlstad for three large silver beakers. The engineer has not heard of the gold nugget, and I don't believe Papa has, either. He only wants to tease the engineer a bit because he knows all the Gräsmark folk are very proud of their mountain.

But if Papa thought he could cheer up Engineer Frykberg he was very much mistaken. The engineer keeps taking out his watch all the while and looking at it; he does not see that there is a big clock on the wall right in front of him. Turning to Mamma, he asks her whether she is absolutely certain that Mamselle Laurell will be home by six.

No, she is not absolutely certain; it might be possible that they were asked to stay for supper. The engineer gets up and walks around the table once or twice. "Well, perhaps I'd better be going," he says. "Fru Lagerlöf knows I've a good twenty miles to drive, and dusk is already falling." He takes out his handkerchief again and speaks in a voice so doleful that Mamma really feels sorry for him.

"Couldn't you just as well stop here overnight?" she says. "We always keep a fire going in the office, and there are beds and plenty of warm bedding; so it wouldn't be any trouble to us."

When Mamma makes that suggestion, the engineer becomes reanimated. He stuffs his handkerchief into his pocket and beams on her. Then Mamma asks him about his mother. Does she still live with him and manage his house?

"Yes; but she is old and of late has become rather untidy about the house."

"Don't you think it is time you look for a wife, Engineer Frykberg?"

The engineer does not answer. Flushing with embarrassment, he nervously pulls out his handkerchief once more. Mamma and Papa exchange glances and shake their heads. They don't know what to do with him.

Then Papa says: "I'll tell you what, Frykberg. The children always go coasting at this hour. Wouldn't you like to go along and help them steer? Perhaps you may meet Lovisa and Aline while you're out."

This he is delighted to do, and Anna, Emma Laurell, Gerda, and I take him with us. But first we ask him if he isn't going to put on his fur coat, but he says he won't bother, as he has a thick, warm homespun suit on and doesn't need the heavy pelt.

The moment he sees our sled he says it is much too small for coasting. He selects instead a clipper sled, the kind that is used to haul wood from the forest. He pushes it along the avenue and down the hill as far as the Resting Stone. When we sit on that clipper sled it takes us down the hill with the speed of lightning. Engineer Frykberg steers in a way that makes the sled fairly fly. There is no danger of its bumping into a snow bank and overturning, as often happens when we ourselves steer. It is the best toboggan ride we've ever had.

We coast down the hill many times. It is so kind of Engineer Frykberg to steer the heavy sled down to the Resting Stone again and again for our pleasure. We chatter to him about everything under the sun, and he responds. We have become such good friends and feel as much at home with him as with Daniel or Johan.

It is wonderful to be out this evening! The bushes and trees are covered with hoarfrost. It lies so thick upon spruce and birch that they hang down over the road, forming a white roof over us. Emma Laurell says it reminds her of the cathedral in Karlstad. Engineer Frykberg then asks her if she has been to Karlstad, and she tells him that she was born there. And that is how he learns that Emma is not our sister, but Aline's. And Emma asks him if he is not a surveyor; for she remembers having met him in Karlstad at a party in her home when her father was living and was the chief surveyor at Karlstad. And Engineer Frykberg is delighted to hear that Emma is Aline's sister and that she remembers him.

Anna says that we must go in now, as it is getting dark; but we could have stayed out coasting all night. Engineer Frykberg lets Gerda and me ride home, for he sees that we are too tired to walk. We think Engineer Frykberg is the nicest old gentleman we have ever met—except Papa, of course.

We children are not so stupid but that we can see he is in love with Aline. That is why he won't leave before she returns. But we don't believe Aline would have Engineer Frykberg; for he is too old and ugly. We feel so sorry for him because he isn't young and good-looking.

Just think! We have been out coasting for several hours, and when we come home supper is ready and on the table. All we have to do is to sit down and eat.

Immediately after supper Papa says: "On Saturday evenings at this hour I usually play a game of camphio with the children. Won't you join us, Engineer Frykberg? It would be a pleasure to the children if you would."

Engineer Frykberg is ready at once. So we bring out the counters and the camphio cards, and then we all sit down round the dining-room table—all except Mamma, who does not care for card games.

Papa and Engineer Frykberg are so amusing when they try to outwit each other, as regular camphio players always do. Anna, Emma Laurell, Gerda, and I are having such a good time laughing at them!

We laugh and chatter so loudly that we do not hear when the driver comes back from Gårdsjö. In fact, we are not aware that Aunt Lovisa and Aline have returned until the door opens and they come in. They are wearing big fur overcoats, which are white with frost. It is bitterly cold, they say—fully thirty-five degrees below zero. If Uncle Kalle had not lent them heavy fur coats they would have frozen to death. They received a hearty welcome at Gårdsjö. Uncle and Aunt insisted on their staying for supper; so they couldn't very well refuse.

When Aline comes in, Engineer Frykberg rises

from the card table and withdraws to the chimney corner. She does not see him until she has removed her wraps.

"Ah! So Engineer Frykberg is here," she says, extending the tips of her fingers.

She is not unfriendly, but she draws herself up to her full height and throws back her head like Fru Hwasser at the Royal Dramatic Theatre when she plays the part of a queen addressing a lackey.

And Aline Laurell, as she stands there, looks ravishingly beautiful. Her colour is fresh, and her hair glistens with hoarfrost, while her large grey eyes flash the way they do when she is in high spirits. I feel that Aline Laurell is superior to us; she is a refined city girl, accustomed to associating with bishops and governors, while we are only plain country folk.

As for Engineer Frykberg—Aline is so far above him that he seems to shrivel and grow smaller and smaller as he looks at her. Besides, he is so unkempt, with his long beard and his homespun clothes. As he shakes hands with her, he stands there, awkward and mute. Mamma, however, comes to his rescue.

"Engineer Frykberg has come to buy oats," she explains. "He has been so nice to the children, and has coasted with them for hours. We have asked him to stop with us overnight, as he has a long journey home."

We want to rush forward and tell Aline what fun

we have had; but we don't dare because she is so stiff and stand-offish. She is like a drawn bow, and we are afraid we'll get an arrow through our bodies if we come too near.

"No, Engineer Frykberg couldn't very well drive home on a cold night like this," says Aline, with that condescending Fru Hwasser air.

Aline must think that her father is still living and that she is standing in their elegant mansion in Karlstad receiving all the humble surveyors of the countryside, who have been invited to a collation at the chief surveyor's home.

Engineer Frykberg remains awkwardly silent. He takes out his large red handkerchief and wipes his forehead, then looks at his watch.

"Aye, Frykberg, you are right," says Papa. "It is almost eleven o'clock. Now that the wanderers have come home we'd better be thinking of bed."

Next morning when Maja comes into the nursery to make the fire, she tells us it is forty degrees below zero. "It is impossible to heat the rooms; so you might as well stay in bed, children."

But we get up all the same. We have never felt cold so severe; it is as if we had moved up to the North Pole. When we come downstairs we find the windowpanes in all the rooms covered with a thick coating of frost. Only a little daylight comes through, and the rooms are icy cold!

The thermometer, which hangs outside one of the windows, cannot be seen, but there is a clear spot in the pane through which we see that the mercury has crept down into the bulb.

The housekeeper says we can't have any spiced bread for breakfast, as every loaf is frozen hard as stone. Nor can we have any butter; for that, too, is frozen solid!

We want to go out and feel what forty degrees below zero is like, but are not permitted. We are not even allowed to touch the doorknob with our bare hands. For if one touches iron when it is forty degrees below zero, it burns like red-hot coals and takes off the skin.

Anyhow, we think it marvellous to experience so sharp a cold. Not even Papa and Mamma, nor the old housekeeper, have ever before known it to be forty degrees below zero at Mårbacka.

We are so completely taken up with the weather that we have entirely forgotten Engineer Frykberg, who was so kind to us the previous evening. But when we are about to sit down to breakfast, Anna asks us if we are not going to wait for the engineer.

"Engineer Frykberg has gone," says Mamma. "When he learned that it was forty below, he got up at once and left for home. He had to go, he said, to look after his pigs and sheep or they would freeze to death. He had no time even to say good-bye."

"But isn't it dangerous to drive so many miles in such weather?" Aline asks.

Papa gives a laugh. "Aye, aye, Aline, it is high time you had a change of heart! I wonder whose fault it was that he went away?"

"Oh, but Uncle," Aline protests, "you can't say that I was not friendly to him!"

"There was a chilliness of at least forty degrees below zero in that friendliness," Papa replies.

And I believe that Papa, and Mamma, too, for that matter, are displeased with Aline. Afterward we children said among ourselves that Aline couldn't possibly care for a man who is so old and ugly; but, anyhow, we feel sorry for him.

I wonder if it was not his intention to freeze himself to death when he set out with the thermometer at forty degrees below? I expect to hear that he never reached home alive. It would be so romantic, as Emma Laurell would say.

X
MAJA RÅD

W<small>E ALWAYS</small> look forward with joy to the coming of Maja Råd the seamstress. Twice a year we get new dresses. Every spring we get a cotton frock, and every autumn we get a woollen frock. All our frocks are homespun. It is Mamma who spins the yarn and makes the dyes; she selects the colours and the designs, and also sets up the loom. She is awfully clever at such things.

When we were small children Mamma made all our dresses herself, but now that we are big girls she does not trust herself to do it without the help of Maja Råd. Maja Råd does the sewing in Aunt Lovisa's room, and Auntie likes to have her there, for then she has company all day long and forgets to think of the things that trouble her.

Mamma always sits in Auntie's room when Maja Råd is here, and helps her with the sewing. Aline

95

and Emma Laurell, Anna, Gerda, and I are here also. Gerda is too little to make anything but doll dresses; but she does them so well that Maja Råd declares she'll be a great seamstress one of these days. Anna, too, is clever at sewing, but Emma Laurell and I are regular botchers. We can't tell the right side of the cloth from the wrong side; therefore we are given only the simplest things to do, such as sewing skirt seams and binding them. But all the same, Emma and I are glad that Maja Råd is here, because we don't have to do any reading or arithmetic.

When Maja Råd comes to the house we move a large folding table into Auntie's room, on which she lays the big bolts of cloth and does the cutting. She always makes sure, before cutting into the cloth, which is the right side and which the reverse. For she is a trained seamstress who has served her apprenticeship with a tailor.

Maja Råd takes a German fashion magazine called *Der Bazar*, which comes out once a month. We look through it every day that she is here and pick out the prettiest models both for our cotton and our woollen frocks. Maja Råd thinks we ought to choose simpler models to go by and says we can't expect a dress, when finished, to look as pretty as it does in the picture.

She doesn't understand German, neither do we. The only foreign language Aline teaches is French, because it is the only one she knows. We wonder how Maja Råd manages to do so well with a magazine that is printed in German. This pleases her, for we are supposed to be learned and to do nothing but read from morning to night.

Maja Råd plasters her thin hair tight to her head, and the white scalp shows through the scanty wisps of hair. Her forehead is covered with tiny little wrinkles, and she has freckles the whole year round. We have freckles, too, that come every spring, but they always disappear in the autumn. She wears a hoopskirt, although hoopskirts are no longer the fashion. I often wonder if there is any special reason why she never discards a thing she has once acquired. For instance, the freckles—she can't get rid of those. It's the same with the hoopskirt.

I used to sit and stare at Maja Råd, and wonder if she was made of wood, for she is so dried out. If she were to prick herself with the needles I doubt if she would draw blood. I wish sometimes that she would prick herself so that I could see whether she would bleed.

We used to ask her when she was going to get a sewing machine, and she would always answer, "Never, so long as I can thread a needle."

Maja Råd wears an open-top thimble, the kind tailors use. To be sure, it was a tailor who taught her to sew, and she is such a rapid sewer that neither

Mamma nor Aunt Lovisa nor even Aline can keep up with her. She charges one riksdaler for a day's work, and with the help she has from us she can make a dress in a day. In that way we get our dresses made for a riksdaler apiece, which is very cheap.

The bodices Maja Råd always makes herself, for they are the most important. There must be two front pieces, two underarm, and two for the back. Each of the fronts must have two darts that taper to a point. These are hard to get just right.

A bodice has to set smoothly and fit close to the figure so there won't be a wrinkle anywhere. That is the most difficult part, but Maja Råd can do it, and she thinks that Gerda can learn. But she declares outright that Emma Laurell and I never can learn to make a proper bodice.

Maja Råd rises every morning at six and sits down to sew as soon as she is dressed. She works all day long and won't even stop to go for a walk. Sometimes we coax her to come out with us, but she turns back almost immediately, saying she must earn her pay and can't waste her time running about the country. But we think she says that only because she doesn't like to do anything but sew.

Maja Råd sews also for our cousins at Gårdsjö and for the Noreens at Herrestad and the Nilssons at Visteberg and for Pastor Lindegren's family. At these houses, too, each child gets a new cotton frock in the spring and a new woollen frock in the autumn. So she has about all she can do.

It is a good thing that Maja Råd doesn't gossip. One can say what one likes before her about other families in the parish, and it will not be repeated. Only this much she will say: "If I were to repeat all I hear in one house about the folks in another house, there would soon be an end of all friendship." So it is well that Maja Råd can hold her tongue.

When she is here the housekeeper serves eleven-o'clock coffee to the grown-ups. We children do not drink coffee, but we each get a sandwich. While Maja Råd sips her coffee she tells us the news. For she knows all that happens in the parish and likes to talk of the things that can do no harm to anyone if told—as, for instance, who is to marry and who has died, who is to give a party and who is to go to America.

And when she has been here so long that all her topics of conversation are used up, Gerda gets out her book of a hundred riddles, which she got one Christmas, and lets Maja Råd and the rest of us guess the riddles.

"Do you know what it is that runs and runs and never moves from the spot?" That Maja Råd knows as well as we do, but she always says she doesn't know the answer—just to please Gerda. She never guesses any of Gerda's riddles, although she hears them regularly, twice a year. And, of course, we all laugh at her for being so stupid.

Maja Råd has told us that even as a child her heart was set on learning to make dresses. In fact, it was her only wish. She did not care to tend sheep, like her brothers and sisters; nor did she like to cook or scrub floors or churn butter or bake bread. She only wanted to sew.

When she grew up she cared nothing for dancing and had no desire to marry, for she did not want babies. Her sole ambition was to become a dress-maker.

She begged her mother to let her go down to the Mamselles Myrin, who were clever at all kinds of needlework. But when she appealed to them, they said it was impossible to teach a poor crofter's girl anything so difficult and exacting as the making of dresses.

So Maja Råd had to do what others of her class did: herd cattle, pitch manure, prepare meals, and, in summer, go with livestock up the säters. But just as she had given up all hope of ever becoming a seamstress, her sister married a corporal who was a tailor. When the brother-in-law heard that Maja Råd's greatest desire was to make dresses, he offered to teach her himself. He taught her how to take measurements and how to draft patterns and cut cloth, how to do fitting and how to make buttonholes, and everything else which she needed to know.

And when she had learned all that her brother-in-law could teach her, she began to make dresses for children and young peasant girls with whom she need not be overparticular. But, all the same, Maja Råd did her level best to please them.

All went well with her from the start, and before long her reputation as a dressmaker spread throughout the countryside. The parlourmaid at Mårbacka then had Maja Råd make a dress for her. The dress was so well made that when Fru Lagerlöf saw it she sent for her. From Mårbacka she went to Gårdsjö, and from Gårdsjö to Herrestad, and from Herrestad to Visteberg and also to Halla. And even from the leading families of Sunne and Ransäter came requests that she sew for them.

I love to hear Maja Råd tell how, after years of longing to become a dressmaker, she finally got her chance to learn. And now she does not have to carry water or scrub floors or pitch manure; she can devote her time to the work she loves and for which she is best fitted.

I also love to hear about Christine Nilsson: of how she once went about the country fairs playing the violin and singing and how she afterward became a great prima donna and sang at the Grand Opera in

Paris. I have just read of how the students in New York unharnessed the horses from her carriage and themselves drew her carriage through the streets to her hotel. She was so touched by this tribute to her voice that tears of gratitude filled her eyes.

I am always moved when I hear about those who have struggled against great odds and who, in the end, have attained success.

XI
GOING TO CHURCH

Driving to church on a Sunday morning is great fun. We go up a steep hill before we come to the level stretch of road that leads to the church. Jansson whips up the horses so that we drive in at full gallop. There are always a lot of people seated on the low wall around the church, waiting for the service to begin. They all jump to their feet and bow or curtsy when they see the folks from Mårbacka coming. And this, we think, is very nice of them. There are also groups of people standing on the church knoll and in the road, and they quickly fall back as we drive by. Mamma shouts to the coachman to drive carefully; but Papa, who sits with hat in hand, greeting people to right and left, only laughs; for he knows that Jansson won't run over anyone.

We pull up before the parish hall, where there is a small dressing room to which one can retire after a drive, to smooth one's hair and straighten one's crumpled clothing. But no one bothers to go in there except the gentry.

We usually meet Aunt Augusta Wallroth in the dressing room, and Cousins Hilda and Emilia, and Fru Nilsson from Visteberg, with her daughters, Emilie and Ingrid. While in the parish room we laugh and chatter about all sorts of things; but when we come out on the church knoll we are quiet and solemn, for that is the custom in East Ämtervik. Mamma always brings with her a large bouquet of flowers on the drive to church, and coming out from the parish room, she goes over to the cemetery to place the flowers on Grandmother's grave. Anna and I go with her, of course. Mamma clears away the dry leaves which have fallen on the turf and straightens the little brier bush. Then she says a prayer and places the bouquet of flowers on the grave.

I once had a little sister whom I have never seen. Mamma and Papa were very fond of her. She lies beside Grandmother. Mother always takes two or three of the prettiest flowers from the bouquet and places them at one end of the mound. I understand for whom they are meant; but I wonder if Mamma really wishes she had another little daughter living. I should think she had all she could do to patch, darn, knit, and sew for Anna, Gerda, and me; then how would she be able to do for any more daughters?

From the cemetery we go direct to the church.
If on the way Mamma happens to meet some peasant
woman of her acquaintance, she stops to speak to
her. If, for instance, she should see Mother Katrina
of Västmyr, or Mother Britta of Gata, or Mother
Katrina, the daughter of Jan Larssa of Ås, or Mother
Maja of Prästbol, or Mother Kerstin from Dar-ner-
i-Mårbacka, she stops to greet them and exchange
a few words. Mamma has attended weddings and
funerals at their cottages and is familiar with all
their circumstances; so she knows what to say to one
and all.

After we have entered the church we go at once to
our seats in the first row of pews of the gallery, for
that is where the gentry usually sit. Our pews are on
the left side of the gallery. It would never do to take
seats on the right side, because that side is reserved
for the men. If all the pews are occupied on the
women's side and there is plenty of room on the opposite side, rather than go over there one would
stand through the entire service.

As soon as we are seated in our pew, we bow our
heads and say a silent prayer. After that, we look
about us. We look to see whether Sexton Melanoz is
at the organ and if Herr Alfred Schullström, who
keeps the only shop in Älvvik, sits beside him as
usual, and if all the church wardens are in their
places, on the narrow bench in the chancel, and if

Fru Lindegren of Halla is in the rectory pew, just below the pulpit. We also look to see whether Jan Asker, the beadle, stands at the door of the sacristy, waiting for the stragglers to come in so that they may begin the service. Then we look to see whether the chant numbers have been properly posted on the hymnboard and whether the coat tails of the organ blower stick out from behind the organ, to assure ourselves he is in his place. When in this manner we have found that all is as it should be, we have nothing with which to occupy our minds during the entire service.

It is considered very exclusive to sit in the front row of the gallery, but the place has certain drawbacks. You can't hear anything the pastor in the pulpit below is saying, except the first words of the altar service, including the confession of sins—that you can hear, of course. But all that comes after is swallowed up by the walls and the ceiling. You hear that someone is speaking, though you cannot distinguish the words; at least, we children do not know what is being said.

When the organ plays, we hear it, but it is not much joy to us, for no one dares sing in the church at East Ämtervik. We sit with the hymnbook in our hands and follow the words, but have not the courage to take up the tune. Once, when I was little, and did

not know what was proper, I sang a whole stanza as
loud as I could, for I think it a joy to sing, and at
home I sing all day long. But when the next stanza
was about to begin, Anna leaned over and whispered
into my ear: "Don't you see how Emilie Nilsson is
staring at you because you are singing?"

The only person who sings in church is Jan of
Ruffluck Croft, and he is not quite right in his head.
I sometimes wonder if Sexton Melanoz doesn't get
furious at the congregation for letting him play hymn
after hymn without their singing a note. For, all of
a sudden, he does something to the organ that makes
it rumble and roar and bellow loud enough to raise
the roof off the church. Sexton Melanoz is a merry
soul and up to all sorts of pranks; so it would be just
like him.

But I am sorry I can't hear the sermon. Pastor
Lindegren is a neighbor of ours and a good friend.
He is always so nice to us children, and, besides, he is
very good-looking. But he's handsomer than ever
when he stands in the pulpit and preaches. He speaks
with much fervor and strikes out with his hand, in
which he holds a large white handkerchief, and the
longer he talks the handsomer he grows. Almost
every time he preaches he is moved to tears. And
then I wonder if he weeps because we do not mend
our ways and become converted despite all his

pleading. To us who sit in the front row of the gallery, and can't hear a word, it seems easy to be guided by him.

The grown-ups are so used to being bored that to them it doesn't matter; but we children become restless and find it hard to pass the time. Emilia Wallroth has told me that she usually counts the spikeheads in the ceiling during the sermon. Ingrid Nilsson says that she watches the old farmers down in the nave to see how many times they offer one another snuff. Her sister Emilie adds the numbers on the hymnboard, and when the addition is done she subtracts and multiplies and divides. She says as long as she does this no sinful thoughts can enter her head. It would be worse if she sat gazing at Hilda Wallroth's pretty bonnet and wishing she had one like it. Anna tells us that she passes the time learning the hymns by heart, and this we all think ever so much better than to multiply and subtract.

As for me, I neither reckon nor look to see who takes snuff. I picture to myself what would happen if the church spire were struck by lightning and the building set on fire. All the people would get into a panic and start running, and they would trample one another nearly to death. At that moment I would rise up from my seat in the front row of the gallery and command them to be calm. And then I would order them to fall in line, and say as in *Fritiof's*

Saga: "Now from the temple down to the strand they march, hand linked to hand." Then I would put out the fire, and be lauded for my bravery in the *Värmland News*.

After the service, Mamma, Anna, and I pay a visit to the Mamselles Myrin—two old ladies who live in the garret of the schoolhouse, which is next door to the church. Anna and I would be afraid to live so near the churchyard. We would not dare to go out except in broad daylight—and never after dark; for then the ghosts in the churchyard might come and spirit us away.

The Mamselles Myrin once lived at Herrestad, but that was long before our time. Now they are very poor, but no one is supposed to know it. One defers to them as though they were still the owners of Herrestad Manor.

The stairs leading to the Mamselles Myrin's room have been newly scoured and strewn with fresh juniper twigs; for the old ladies are expecting the gentry who attended church to call. Mamma always carries in her reticule a bottle of cream or a pat of butter, when paying a visit to the Mamselles Myrin, which she leaves in their kitchen in passing. On the stair we nearly always meet some peasant woman with a package under her arm, which she smuggles into the kitchen.

The Mamselles Myrin have a large, attractive

living room, where they sit in their comfortable wicker chairs, dressed in their old-time finery to receive their guests. They do not know of the provisions left in the kitchen. Both sisters are wearing large black tulle caps, and voluminous mantillas over their frocks. Mamselle Marie Myrin is tall and stately and her hair is snow-white, but her fingers are bent and swollen with gout. Mamselle Rosa Myrin, on the contrary, is petite and dark-haired; her hands are small and shapely, and she can open and close them with ease.

As soon as Mamma enters the Mamselles Myrin's living room, she begins to admire their curtains, their table covers, their antimacassars, and their bedspreads, all of which are worked in shell stitch by their own hands. Mamselle Rosa then tells her how many table covers and curtains have been ordered; they have more orders than they can possibly fill. It is remarkable how enthusiastic everyone in East Ämtervik is about shell-stitching! And then Mamma tells her that this is just what she has come for; she would like so much to have a large round cover for the sofa-table in the dining room. But perhaps the Mamselles Myrin have so many orders on hand, it would not be possible to get a table cover from them? Mamselle Marie looks a bit doubtful, but Mamselle Rosa quickly pulls out a drawer of her bureau filled to the very edge with shell-stitching—Mamma has only to choose, she can have as many covers as she wishes. And Mamma is so glad that she does not have to go home empty-handed. She orders not only a cover for the round table, but two antimacassars for the rocking chair as well.

When she has settled for these and is about to leave, the old ladies protest that, since she has made so large a purchase, they would like to offer her a cup of coffee. Mamma declines, with many thanks; but the old ladies are so insistent that she finally decides to stay.

The Mamselles Myrin have a brother who is a rich ironmaster and who lives on Bada Foundry Estate, in Lysvik. Ironmaster Myrin has three daughters who sometimes come to see their old aunts, and who always supply them with quantities of small cakes and spiced coffee bread, in order that their aunts may have something in the house to offer their Sunday visitors. The Mamselles Myrin are so generously supplied with these small cakes the whole year round that they never have to do any baking themselves.

Anna and I are glad when the coffee tray comes in, for on it is a big plate of fancy cakes and rusks, which look very good to us. But just then Mamma asks the Mamselles Myrin when their nieces last paid them a visit. And the old ladies answer that they have not been there since a year ago the previous autumn.

Mamma takes only a couple of dry rusks with her coffee, and warns us not to be greedy and pile our saucers full of cakes. We must remember that the Mamselles Myrin themselves might want some portion of the good cakes which their nieces have sent them. And when Mamma says that, we each take only two of the very smallest cookies.

When we come home we are glad that we have been to church. Although we were not allowed to sing the hymns, and could not hear the sermon, and were only permitted to eat two small cakes at the Mamselles Myrin's, yet we feel that Mamma is right when she says that it is good to spend a few hours in the House of God.

XII
THE KISS

ALINE LAURELL is going to leave us in the autumn, and we children feel dreadfully about it. She says that she lacks the required knowledge to carry us further. She knows no foreign language but French, and we should have lessons also in English and German. Nor is she so well grounded in music as she ought to be. Of course it is sweet of Aline to go that we may have more learning than she can give us; but just the same, we shall miss her very much.

Aline has a cousin, Elin Laurell, for whom she has a high regard. This cousin knows both English and German and is also a fine musician. She is to be our governess when Aline goes. We have heard that Elin is at least thirty years of age, and since she is so old she won't care to romp with us children or take part in any of our amusements; and, besides, she is not pretty. I saw her once at a party at Pastor Unger's, and I thought her downright ugly.

Aline will move to West Ämtervik, to be governess to the small children of the Ungers. They are much younger than we; so it will be easy for her to teach them. Fru Unger is Aline's maternal aunt, and Aline is very fond of her. We wonder if she is leaving Mårbacka because she prefers to live with her aunt.

Emma Laurell is to remain with us a few months more, so as to study with Elin. Next year she goes back to her mother, at Karlstad, to enter a girls' school there. We are glad that Emma at least will stay, for she is like a sister to us.

I don't think Mamma and Papa want Aline to go, though they say nothing to the contrary. Anna suspects that neither of them believes Aline is leaving because she lacks the requisite knowledge to teach us; they think there is something else back of it all. So do I.

Her decision to move was so sudden. In the spring, when she went home for the Easter holidays, there was no talk of her not continuing with us. Nor was anything said about leaving when she returned in August, after the summer holidays.

She got back in time to celebrate Papa's birthday, for there is nothing she enjoys more than to be at Mårbacka on a seventeenth of August. She was in high spirits that day, and afterward, too, as long as we had guests in the house. But they had no sooner departed than she began to talk of going and declared that she was not competent to teach us any more.

We children can see that Aline is not herself. Ever since the day she gave notice she has been irritable and impatient—as if she disliked us. When she gives me a music lesson I actually tremble with fear. I have no talent for music; but Papa and Mamma think I might learn enough to play a waltz or a reel at a party. They say it will be a joy to me in my old age. Aline used to be so patient with me in my efforts at learning to play the piano; but now she becomes furious if I make the least mistake.

One day she came late to the afternoon session. As this was the first time it had occurred in the four years that she had been governess at Mårbacka, we felt uneasy about her. We were to have a lesson in arithmetic this afternoon and had taken out our slates and pencils from the table drawer and were sharpening our pencils while we waited for Aline. Anna said she can't be far away, for when she passed through the bedroom a while ago Aline was there talking with Mamma.

It was a quarter past two when she came into the nursery. We noticed that her face was flushed, as if she were suffering from toothache. She opened the arithmetic and told us what sums to do; then threw herself down on the nursery sofa and burst out crying.

She wept so hard that her body shook, but she did not speak; neither did we.

We sat there, with our slates before us, unable to speak a word of comfort to her whom we loved so much. We were afraid she would resent it if we spoke to her. Nor could we do our sums. It was impossible to think of anything but Aline lying there sobbing her heart out. At last Anna got up and put her slate away and motioned to Gerda and me to do the same. We tiptoed out of the nursery, leaving Emma Laurell alone with her sister.

Anna and I then went out to the garden and sat down on a bench where no one could see or overhear us. Anna was fifteen years old on the second day of September, and as she is very wise Mamma consults with her about everything. Mamma has told Anna that she is anxious about Aline and can't understand why she is leaving. She has asked Anna if she knows what has caused Aline to make this decision. But Anna can't say. Knowing that Aline is used to talking freely to me, Anna wondered if I could recall whether she has said anything in particular about Uncle Kristofer.

That Anna should consult *me* on a serious matter filled me with pride. (She had never done so before.) But I couldn't imagine what it was she wanted to know. What can Aline have said "in particular" about Uncle Kristofer?

Anna gave a sigh. Was I so stupid as not to understand to what she referred? Then, putting the matter plainly, she said: "In the summer when the guests were here, Mamma, Aunt Georgina, and Aunt Augusta wanted to make a match between Uncle Kristofer and Aline Laurell. He had been a bachelor long enough, they thought, and should take advantage of the opportunity to get such a splendid girl as Aline. Now that he had bought a little place near Filipstad, it was especially fitting that he should marry, and Aline was the very wife for him. She was wise and kindly and thrifty, too. She was no spoilsport, but could jest and bandy words, and like himself, loved life and its gaieties."

I was too astonished for words. Anna said further: "I think Mamma and Aunt Georgina must have talked with Uncle Kristofer about Aline, for he has been especially attentive to her this summer. No doubt it was because Uncle Kristofer was so nice to her that she was in such high spirits while he was here. For Uncle Kristofer is a man who, if he chooses, can make any young girl fall in love with him."

Anna, being fifteen, knows more about such things than I know, who am only twelve. It never occurred to me, I said to Anna, that anyone could fall in love with Uncle Kristofer.

"But you must remember," said Anna, "that Uncle Kristofer is a great painter, and a great musician as well. And think how fascinating he is and how much he knows about Italy and Germany. Besides, he is young—only a few years older than Daniel."

While Anna was speaking I recalled to mind two or three incidents which I had not understood before. It was customary, when guests stayed on at Mårbacka after the seventeenth of August, to have some kind of entertainment for them. Sometimes we would remove all the furniture from the dining room, and Uncle Oriel, who had grown up in Enköping, would dance the old folk dances of Uppland. And sometimes Uncle Kristofer would sing a number of Erik Bögh's ditties, or he and Fru Hedda Hedberg would don student caps and sing college songs, and sometimes we would persuade Aunt Nana Hammargren to tell us a ghost story. And I remembered the evening when Uncle Kristofer sat at the piano and improvised. Uncle Oriel, wearing a woman's wide-brimmed bonnet and a mantilla across his shoulders, had sung *Emelie's Heart-throbs*. It had been screamingly funny to see Uncle Oriel, who is sixty years old, play a timid and blushing maiden. When he had finished his song, Uncle Kristofer, who had played his accompaniment, remained seated at the piano. After a little he began to play in a wholly different manner. As he had no notes before him, I asked Aunt Georgina what he was playing. "Sh!" she said; then whispered: "Uncle is improvising."

I didn't know what "improvising" meant, but concluded it must be something remarkable, for all the others were so quiet and looked so solemn. Uncle Kristofer played on and on, and I was astonished at his being able to play all that music without his notes.

While Uncle Kristofer was playing I happened to glance at Aline Laurell. She, like the others, sat motionless; but her face was intensely alive. She seemed to be listening intently, as if someone were speaking to her. At times she would smile, and at times she would drop her eyes and her face would flush. As I looked at her I knew that she understood what Uncle Kristofer was playing as well as though he were speaking to her.

And then on another occasion—Lovisa Day, the twenty-fifth of August, when we celebrate Aunt Lovisa's name-day with theatricals, which she enjoys above everything. That year we gave *The Visit of the Countess*, by Fru Lenngren. This too had been a great success. Aline played the Corpulent Dean. She had stuffed herself out until she was round as a barrel, and had worn a big woolly peruke. Uncle Kristofer had played the Countess in a trailing satin gown and a large white silk shawl. He had worn a big bonnet poised at the back of the head, and a white veil falling over the face.

Uncle Kristofer had grown a full beard while studying art at Düsseldorf, and the beard could not be concealed under a veil. But when he flung his head back and drew himself up, with a gesture of command, we all thought him a perfect Countess and forgot about the beard.

After the performance, while we were changing our clothes in the nursery—for I, too, had a part in the play—I asked Aline if she did not think Uncle Kristofer had been very amusing.

"Amusing! Is that all you can say of him—and he a born actor!" She spoke so sharply it frightened me, and I did not venture to ask her any more questions. Aline continued: "You all think him very amusing. All you care about is to see him dressed up like a clown, so that you may laugh. But I say it's a shame! Your uncle is a genius. He can become a great painter or a great composer or a great actor—whichever he chooses to be. But you care nothing for such things. You only want him to be the jester. Not one among you thinks enough of him to discern the wealth of beauty there is in his soul."

I thought afterward how grand Aline was as she spoke of him. But it never dawned upon me that she loved Uncle Kristofer. And when I told Anna of this, and of the way she looked at him when he played the piano, she thought there was no doubt whatever that Aline was in love with Uncle Kristofer.

Anna thought, moreover, that he proposed to Aline the last day he was here, and that she refused him.

At the last moment something had come between them, though what it was I couldn't imagine. She certainly cared for him still. Anna had seen a letter that came from Filipstad that day, and she thought that Mamma had talked to Aline about Uncle Kristofer, and that is why Aline was late at the arithmetic hour. She would not have cried like that unless she was fond of Uncle Kristofer. And yet she rejected him. I can't make her out.

We ponder a long while over this, but can find no solution to the mystery. Finally we give it up and look instead for pippins dropped from Grandfather's apple tree. I feel as if I have a large tumor on the brain which will not disappear until I have solved the mystery of Aline's strange behavior.

Between six and seven in the evening, Mamma is usually alone in the nursery; so I go in and, taking a textbook off the shelf, sit down and pretend to read, but in reality I do nothing but think of Aline. After a while Nurse Maja comes in to turn down our beds for the night. She is astonished to see me sitting there, bent over a book. "What's the matter, Selma?" she asks. "Have you got back lessons to make up?"

"No," I reply; "but I'm very unhappy because Aline is leaving us."

This is news to Nurse Maja, who is generally posted on all that goes on at Mårbacka. But she, too, is sorry that Mamselle Aline is leaving. "Ah! She is someone it does you good to see around the house."

Nurse Maja thinks a moment; and then she says, "I can't understand why Fru Lagerlöf has given Mamselle Aline notice."

"But Mamma has not given her notice," I say. "It is Aline herself who has given notice. Mamma doesn't even know why she is going."

Nurse Maja falls silent again. She looks thoughtful as she spreads the sheets and tucks in the quilt on Anna's bed. Presently she says: "I too thought that Mamselle Aline would soon be leaving us, but I supposed she'd be off in a different direction."

"Where did you think she was going?"

"Well, you see, Selma, I thought you'd soon be getting another aunt."

I make no reply to this, for I don't like to have Nurse Maja know so much about our affairs. She goes on with her bed-making awhile. Then she remarks with a deep sigh: "Perhaps it is best as it is. Anyhow, she wouldn't be getting much if she got him."

I resent her speaking in that slighting way of Uncle Kristofer. "Why shouldn't he be good enough for Aline, I'd like to know?"

Nurse Maja quickly finishes the beds and comes over to me. "Now, Selma, I'm going to tell you something that I saw on the seventeenth of August." And then Nurse Maja tells me that one of the guests had torn her dress on a gooseberry bush when she was out in the orchard munching berries. Who the guest was, she will not say, only this much will she divulge: The woman was young and pretty—and married. She was not of this parish, and had never been at Mårbacka before. The rest I must guess.

The pretty wife whose name Nurse Maja would not divulge was walking in the orchard with Uncle Kristofer and Fru Lindegren when she tore her dress. She was both vexed and grieved, as one can imagine. The whole length of the sleeve was ripped and must be mended. It would be too embarrassing to go up to the main building among all the guests, to look for a needle and thread. Uncle Kristofer suggested that she step into Papa's office, as no one was there at this time. Fru Lindegren offered to run over to the house for a needle and thread and come back to the office to help her mend the sleeve.

The pretty guest thanked Fru Lindegren for her kindness and followed Uncle Kristofer into the office. It was some little time before Fru Lindegren could find any sewing materials; for on a festal day like this nothing was in its usual place at Mårbacka. But at last she found a sewing basket and hurried down to the office with it, so as not to keep the pretty lady waiting too long.

There is a small round window in the door of the office; it is only a little peephole where the one inside can see to whom he opens. Now, when Fru Lindegren of Halla stood outside the office she glanced through the window to see whether Uncle Kristofer was still there, waiting for her.

And Fru Lindegren saw Uncle Kristofer and the pretty young fru standing in the middle of the room, kissing. Fru Lindegren was at a loss what to do. She couldn't go in and surprise them while they stood kissing; but, on the other hand, the pretty young guest must have a needle and thread to mend her dress. Just then she caught sight of Nurse Maja running across the yard and called to her. She asked Nurse Maja to take the sewing basket to the young fru and help her mend the sleeve she had torn on a gooseberry bush. "But you must rap hard three times before you open the door," she said.

And Maja did so. But before she knocked she peeped in through the small window in the office door. And then she knew why Fru Lindegren wouldn't take the sewing basket in herself. After knocking three times she opened the door as slowly as possible, and when she entered, Uncle Kristofer stood at the window and the pretty young matron stood over by the Dutch stove. He was calm and collected as ever, but she was flushed and her hair was disarranged.

Nurse Maja said she did not dare to speak of this to anyone but me. Whether Fru Lindegren had also been mum, she could not say. "Don't you remember

that Pastor and Fru Lindegren were here the evening
before the company left, and that we saw them home
in the lovely moonlight? And do you remember that
Aline and Fru Lindegren walked together all the
way? Don't you suppose Fru Lindegren took advantage of the occasion to tell Aline about the kiss?"

Anna agreed with me that such must be the case;
for ever since that night Aline has not been herself.
"And don't you think it was because Aline heard
about the kiss that she threw Uncle Kristofer over?"
I said eagerly and with renewed hope.

"Why, of course," she answered, but she did not
seem to be the least bit happy about the discovery.

"And don't you think that was the reason why
Aline became indignant at Uncle Kristofer and decided to leave?"

"Yes," said Anna. "That's as clear as day."

I looked at Anna. Much to my surprise, she did not
appear to be pleased. She sat there quietly instead
of hurrying in to tell the news to Mamma.

"Aren't you going to tell Mamma that we know
why Aline is leaving?" I asked her.

"No," she answered. "I don't believe it would be of
any use in this case. Aline is very strict about things
of that sort. Now she will never marry Uncle Kristofer."

"No, of course not," I said. "But Mamma might
persuade her to stay. She doesn't have to go away

from us simply because Uncle Kristofer kissed a strange lady."

Anna looked at me. I knew that she thought me stupid. "Can't you understand that it is on account of that kiss she is leaving?" said Anna. "As long as she stays here she will think of it every day. It is this she cannot bear, and that is why she is going away."

XIII
THE BALL AT SUNNE

We are thankful that we live in East Ämtervik and not in Sunne. There are more people in Sunne, but they are not so jolly as the East Ämtervik folk. They never have any festivities; they have no brass sextette and no male quartette, and there are not so many who can make a speech or write a poem as there are at East Ämtervik.

The only interest we have in common is the dean. As the pastorate is a large one, the dean cannot invite all the families at the same time; so he usually asks those who live in East and West Ämtervik and Gräsmark at one time, and those who live in Sunne at another time.

In other respects, we have no contact with the Sunne folk. We never meet any of the leading families of Sunne, but we feel instinctively that they consider themselves above us because they live in a larger parish.

Once a year we are invited to a party at the deanery, but we do not meet any of the native sons there. Although we are not acquainted with the first families of Sunne, we have seen them all at the Ämbergshed fair, and know them by sight: the Squire Pettersons of Stöpafors, the Engineer Maules of Sundsberg, the Engineer Igneliuses of Ulvsberg, the Squire Hellstedts of Skarped and Squire Jonsson's family, who live at the "castle" of Sundsvik.

On the seventeenth of August many young men from Sunne come to Mårbacka to dance and to join in the festivities. They must have told the Sunneites that Hilda Wallroth of Gårdsjö and Anna Lagerlöf of Mårbacka have grown up to be the prettiest girls in the whole Fryken valley. At all events, one fine day Papa received a letter from two gentlemen of Sunne, requesting the presence of himself and family at a buffet supper dance.

The dance was to be held in the rooms over Nilsson's general store, which they were to have, rent free, for the evening. The gentlemen were to furnish the beverages and the ladies were to bring coffee, tea, and cakes, or whatever else needed for the supper. It was to be a most unpretentious affair; the only outlay would be a few riksdalers for lights and gratuities.

A similar letter was sent to Gårdsjö, and Aunt

Augusta came over to consult with Mamma and Aunt Lovisa as to what they should contribute. For they were not going to be outdone by the Sunne folk. Aunt Lovisa immediately set the dough for a big bake of fancy bread and cake. They used to have these buffet supper dances when Auntie was young. Not for a moment did she think of going to the ball; she knew very well that she was too old to dance. But she thought it nice there was something jolly to look forward to. It was the same with Gerda and me—we, too, thought it jolly that there was to be a dance, although we were too young to attend.

The day before the dance, as we sat at the dinner table talking about the ball, Papa said: "I think Selma is big enough now to go along with the others."

Papa thought I should be delighted to go to a dance; but indeed I was not. I had been to so many parties in East Ämtervik that I knew well enough how I would fare at the dance in Sunne! "I don't want to go," I promptly answered.

"Why don't you want to go to the ball?" Papa asked me. Then, turning to Mamma, he said, "Has she no dress?"

"Oh, yes," said Mamma. "She has her light grey cashmere dress, which will do well enough."

"How about the proper shoes and stockings?"

"Anna has outgrown the grey cloth shoes she wore at Sister Julia's wedding, and Selma can have those."

"Then," said Papa, "I see no reason why she shouldn't go."

I was seized with dread. I did not know of what I was afraid, but I could imagine no worse calamity than having to go to that Sunne ball!

"But, Papa, I am too young to go to a ball. I'm only thirteen."

"Emilia Wallroth is going," said Auntie, "and she is no older than you are."

When I saw that they were all against me—not only Papa and Mamma, but even Aunt Lovisa—I began to cry.

"My dear child," said Papa, "why do you cry when you are going to have a good time?"

"But I won't have a good time," I whimpered. "No one will dance with me because I am lame."

I was not angry, for ever since the day I played cards with Uncle Wachenfeldt I have kept my temper under control. And Papa wasn't angry, either; only he thought me a strange child.

"But, Papa, you do not know how it feels when all the other girls are invited to dance and you are not. Or when you are asked for just a reel, or by some man no other girl would dance with."

"What nonsense!" said Papa, and his voice sounded terribly stern. "I want my daughters to go to a dance whenever it is possible."

"Gustaf, I think you might let her wait at least

until she is fifteen," said Aunt Lovisa, coming to my aid rather late. It would have been better if she had not mentioned Emilia a moment ago.

"Why, to be sure she may wait," said Papa. "But who knows whether there will be another ball in Sunne then? This is the first one they've had in many years."

I know that Papa hates to see us weep, and that he would be far more likely to let me off if I laughed and looked pleasant. But now I can't stop crying; the tears pour down my cheeks all through the dinner.

And I continue to weep while taking my noonday rest and during the afternoon lessons and while we are out tobogganing, and even when we sit at the round table in the dining room, working. Gerda usually cries a lot when she doesn't know her lessons, but I don't think she has ever kept it up from noon until bedtime.

When Mamma comes to the nursery to hear our evening prayers I choke back the tears long enough to say an "Our Father" and "Lord Bless Us," but I stick at "God Who Cares for Little Children," and "An Angel Watches Over Us."

"Is it only on account of the ball you are crying?" Mamma queries. "Or is there some other reason?"

"Mamma, won't you please ask Papa if I may be excused from going to the dance?"

"Dear child, you know that Papa is only thinking of your pleasure."

"Yes; but I won't be asked to dance, and you know it, Mamma."

"Why, of course you will dance," says Mamma and goes her way.

My first thought on awaking next morning is: "This is the day of the ball," and straightway I fall to weeping again. I did not know the eyes could shed so many tears; there seem to be no end to them!

Anna and Gerda are talking about the ball—who is to open it, and who is to have the first waltz with Anna, and whether the Frökens Maule will dress in white. Anna has done up her hair in curl papers and hopes her curls will stay in until the ball is over. The more they talk of these things, the harder I cry. If I could only stop crying!

"Selma, you mustn't take on so," says Anna. "Your eyes will be red and swollen tonight if you cry like that." I promise not to weep any more; but I can't stop.

Anna, Mamma, and Elin Laurell are busy with their toilettes the whole forenoon. They baste ribbons on their frocks, iron their starched petticoats, and try on their shoes, for they want to look as attractive as possible. Aunt Lovisa thinks it strange that one should go to a ball in high-neck and long sleeves. It was not the correct thing when she was young. But

Mamma says that since Anna and I are only children, our party dresses will do well enough.

Later in the forenoon I step into the dining room to see Papa. I find him seated in the rocker, as usual, reading the *Värmland News*. I walk straight up to him and place one foot on the rocker and one hand on his shoulder.

"What is it now?" he asks, turning to me.

"Papa, may I be excused from going to the ball?" I beg sweetly, for it has occurred to me that, by asking in all humility, I can persuade him to let me off. I also intend to remind him that it was on his account I read the Bible and, considering what I did for him, he ought to let me stay at home.

"You know, Papa, that I shall not be invited to dance, as I'm so lame that no one will dance with me." That is as far as I get when I burst into tears again.

Without a word, Papa rises from his chair and, taking me by the hand, leads me out to the kitchen. He asks the housekeeper to make me a nice thick sandwich with plenty of cheese on top—and goes his way.

Now I know that he will insist on my going to the ball. I feel like throwing the sandwich on the floor; but I dare not give way to my temper, or the wild beast in me will break loose again.

I conduct myself properly in every way, but I continue to cry. I weep at the dinner table; I weep afterward; I weep when we dress for the ball. In fact, I weep all the time until we are seated in the sleigh and the robes are tucked around us.

Then, at last, the tears must have known that nothing was gained by falling. As we drive into Sunne I sit in the sleigh—dry-eyed. I am wearing my grey cashmere dress with the blue border and Anna's light grey cloth shoes, with the red silk laces. At the throat I have a pretty bright red rosette, which was a Christmas present from Uncle Kalle (he always gives us such dainty things for Christmas). Aunt Lovisa has dressed my hair so that it lies smooth and even, and twisted it into a big knot at the nape of the neck.

But what does it matter how I am dressed since my face is covered with blotches and my eyes are red and swollen from weeping! I look so hideous that no one would ask me to dance, even if I did not limp.

There is a reception room opening into the ball-room, and as we come in the Wallroth girls tell us the Frökens Maule are dressing; that they are going to wear sheer white frocks, and, to keep their skirts from wrinkling, two maids carried them to Sunne on hangers suspended from a pole, and we all think it a grand idea.

"Oh, they can do that who have only a short distance to go!" says Anna.

Anna and Hilda are such pretty girls that no mat-

ter how the others may deck themselves out, they
can never look so beautiful as these two girls. When
the Frökens Maule come in I must admit that their
dresses are lovely, and the girls are pretty, too; but
they can't hold a candle to Anna and Hilda for
beauty!

Emilia Wallroth is not at all good-looking, but
everyone says she has charm. Emilia is engaged for
every dance. Nobody thinks of her plainness; for
she is so lively and entertaining that every man would
dance with her, even if she were lame.

The reception room is now crowded with matrons
and girls. The music strikes up, so everyone must be
here. It is the brass sextette from East Ämtervik
that is playing, for they have no musicians in Sunne.
Squire Vilhelm Stenbäck of Björsbyholm comes into
the reception room. He says: "Since there has been
no ball in Sunne for at least twenty years, I propose
that we open this festal occasion with a promenade
polonaise, as is customary at state balls."

Then the elderly gentlemen come into the reception
room and offer an arm to the elderly ladies—Fru
Maule, Fru Hellstedt, Fru Pettersson, Fru Bergman,
Fru Wallroth, and Fru Lagerlöf; and they go into
the ballroom arm in arm. The young gentlemen now
come in and ask the young ladies for the opening
dance. There is no one left in the reception room but
old Mamselle Eriksson of Skäggeberg and me. And

Mamselle Eriksson is at least fifty years old and has thin yellow braids coiled around her ears and long yellow teeth.

There is a gentleman here we haven't seen before. He is in uniform and is said to be the inspector of Kil railway station. He is a stranger, apparently, and when he comes into the reception room to look for a dancing partner, and finds no one but Mamselle Eriksson and me, I wonder which one he will choose. But he turns away at once without taking either of us. Here we sit—Mamselle Eriksson and I—motionless and silent. But all the same I am glad she is here so that I am not left all alone.

I think it is just as well that no one asks me to dance, for now Papa will know that it is the truth that nobody wants to dance with me. It is small consolation, however, for I am having a dreary time.

I wonder who could have induced Mamselle Eriksson of Skäggeberg to come to the ball. For surely she did not come of her own accord!

When the promenade polonaise is over and the dancers return to the reception room, both young and old are in gay spirits. Mamma sits down on the sofa, between Fru Maule and Fru Hellstedt, and they laugh and chat as if they were old friends. Anna sits down by the side of Hilda Ignelius, and whispers to her, and Hilda Wallroth comes in, arm in arm, with Julia Maule.

Afterward there are waltzes, polkas, and reels, waltzes, polkas, and reels—over and over again. Anna and Hilda and Emilia, of course, are in demand for every dance. They are full of life and merriment. Hilda comes over to me and says something I should be glad to hear. She suggests that I go into the ball-room with them and watch the dancers.

But that I don't wish to do. How to avoid it, I do not know; but Anna quickly comes to the rescue: "You'd better not talk to Selma, or she might start crying again."

After the promenade polonaise Mamma and the other matrons dance no more, but they go back to the ballroom to watch the young folks dance. Once more the reception room is entirely deserted, save for me and Mamselle Eriksson. We two remain in our seats the whole evening.

I try to think of all the people who are more unfortunate than I am: the sick; the poor; the blind. Why should you grieve because you are not asked to dance at a ball? What if you were blind?

I wonder whether this is a punishment for something I have said or done, or if it is a lesson in humility. I remember the story of Mamselle Brorström that Papa used to tell; of how some students at the gymnasium in Karlstad invited her to the Market Fair Ball and let her sit there alone the whole evening. She must have thought it strange that she was so unattractive that no one would dance with her. For that is just what I am thinking of myself now.

Next morning, at the breakfast table, Mamma, Elin Laurell, Emma, and Anna tell Papa of the good time they had at the ball last night, and how well everything went off. I say nothing, for I have nothing to say. When Anna has named all with whom she had danced, Papa asks how Selma fared.

"Selma wasn't asked to dance," Mamma replies. "She is too young, you know."

Papa sits musing a while. Then he says: "Don't you think, Louise, that we should write to Stockholm to see if the Afzeliuses can take Selma another winter and let her attend the institute? She improved so much the last time she was there. I should like to see her well and strong before I die."

My eyes nearly pop out of my head. Perhaps Papa feels conscience-stricken because he made me go to the ball last night? Perhaps that is why he wants to send me to Stockholm?

There's no one so nice as my Papa!

XIV
ELIN LAURELL

ALINE LAURELL has come back to pay us a visit;
we have not seen her since she moved to West Ämtervik last autumn. Aline is her own sweet self again,
though perhaps a trifle thinner. But she looks well
and happy. All the old unpleasantness seems to have
been forgotten.

Papa, Mamma, Elin Laurell, Anna, Gerda, and I
are all out on the porch to welcome her, and she hugs
and kisses us all—except Papa, of course. Anna and
Gerda seem to be as glad to see her as I am, and she
kisses them just as affectionately as she kisses me.
It is well that Aline does not know they think more
of Elin than they do of her.

They say, those two, that Elin is such a pleasant
teacher and so nice about the lessons; that she is not
so strict as Aline, and doesn't give us such long lessons to learn; nor does she get angry if we cannot

answer all her questions. But I don't care about shorter lessons! I like Aline the best, anyhow, and no one can make me care more for Elin.

But I must confess that it is difficult not to like Elin. To be sure, she is pleasing and tells us many interesting things. Sometimes she chats with us during school hours until there is little time left for our lessons. This pleases Anna and Gerda, of course. I also think her entertaining, but I don't believe her way is right. Certainly, Aline did not teach us in that way.

When Elin examines our papers, she sometimes passes over a mistake without marking it; but if I speak of this to Anna, she says it doesn't matter. "I learn much more from Elin than I learned from Aline," she declares; "for Elin knows more than is printed in books."

Anna no doubt is right about that, but just the same I don't want to like Elin, I would rather be faithful to Aline. It is a good thing that Elin is plain. Her nose is too short. It looks as if the tip had been cut off, and her complexion is sallow, and she has a wart on one cheek. And besides, she has a double chin, like Field Marshal Klingspor in the story of *Ensign Stål*. But she has a beautiful head of fair hair which is always well dressed, and I must say that she has a tall, graceful figure. Then, too, she has a beautiful voice, and there is something about her that's different. Now when Mamma comes into a room you know by her manner and bearing that she is from Filipstad, for there is something about her of its iron and its forges; and when Aline comes into a room she brings with her something of Karlstad; of its schools and its gay social life. But when Elin enters a room she brings the whole world with her. She is equally at home in Greece and in Egypt; in Greenland and in Australia. She knows what people are thinking wherever human beings are to be found. She knows so much about the ancients, too, and above all, she keeps in touch with everything modern.

Elin, unlike Aline, is not popular with men. No young men come to the house now, as they did when Aline was here. But old gentlemen like Papa and Engineer Noreen love to talk with Elin because of her knowledge of world affairs and because she is not afraid to say what she thinks. She even dares to dispute with Papa about gospel-mongers and itinerant preachers; but she does it with such good humour and makes such witty retorts that he cannot get angry.

Her great delight, however, is to tease the boys. Elin is spending her Christmas holidays with us. As she left home only a month ago, she does not wish to incur the expense of another journey so soon.

I believe that Daniel and Johan find her good company, for they stay around the house now more than they used to. She chaffs them about all sorts of things. But when she declares that girls have as good brains as boys and can learn to do the same things, they get awfully mad. Daniel is not so fiery, but Johan always challenges her to prove her statements. When she is unable to hold her own with him she jumps up and tries to rumple his hair. He darts out of her reach, and then a wild chase begins—first round the table and then through the whole house.

But in a little while they are good friends again. I don't think the boys have ever had more fun than they had during those Christmas holidays. After dinner Elin usually goes to Aunt Lovisa's room to cheer her up a bit. With her, Elin discusses serious matters. Aunt Lovisa is a firm believer in predestination and maintains that what happens to a person has been ordained from the beginning, and that nothing can alter it. If one is destined to marry he will marry, and if one is not, try as much as he will, he must remain single to the end of his days.

"Does this rule apply to all things, both big and little?" Elin asks her, "or is it unalterable only in such weighty matters as marriage and death?"

"It applies to all things," Aunt Lovisa answers.

"In that case," says Elin, "it is useless to pray. For if everything is ordained from the beginning, it is futile to ask God to grant favors."

Aunt Lovisa is at a loss for an answer. "Well, you

see, Elin, that is too difficult for me to explain, for I haven't your good head, Elin."

But just the same, Auntie finds these talks with Elin stimulating. So, you see, it is not easy to dislike Elin. I'm not unfriendly, but I enter into no discussions with her. For it is through these talks with Elin that one learns to like her.

If, in addition to being clever and quick-witted, Elin were also young and pretty like Aline, she would be just what I should like to be when I am grown. So, naturally, it is rather hard for me not to be untrue to Aline.

But now that Aline has come I'm glad I have been faithful to her and have never told Elin things I wouldn't tell anyone else. I have never told her about *Oceola* or my reading of the Bible so that Papa might get well.

Elin has been kind to me all the time. She tried at first to make me talk to her freely, as I talked to Aline, but she soon gave that up. And when I cried so terribly at having to go to the Sunne ball, Elin did not lift a finger to help me. When she and I happen to be alone in the nursery we sit there, sometimes for hours, without exchanging a word. So Elin must have seen that I am trying to dislike her.

The second day Aline was here she looked at me strangely and asked why I was so silent—was I not feeling well? The third day, after dinner, she asked me if I would not like to go for a walk. But she did not include any of the others. I was glad of a chance to be alone with Aline. "We'll have a pleasant hour together," I thought; "just we two," as Aline used to say, as though she and I were of the same age.

She was silent as we walked down the avenue, and when we came to the road she pulled off my mitten and drew my hand into her muff, between her two warm hands.

"My dear child," she said, "how cold you are!"

Aline always used to draw my hand into her muff when we went out together, for it has always been hard for me to keep warm. I am glad that she has taken my hand into her muff once more.

"Now you must tell me," she said, "how you are getting on with your writing."

"But, Aline, don't you remember that I told you I wouldn't write stories until I grew up?"

"There is something I must say to you," Aline began rather hesitantly. "Now don't be angry with me—I have thought that perhaps it was wrong for me to let you talk so much about your ambition to write."

"Why, Aline?"

"Well, you see, I may have been partly to blame for your indulging these fancies. But I thought it might be possible that you had inherited a little talent for writing. Your paternal aunt, Nana Hammargren, is a very clever *raconteuse*, and your maternal uncle Kristofer is a remarkably gifted man, as far as I am able to judge. And besides you are related to the poet Tegnér."

"Are we related to Tegnér?"

"Don't you know you are?" said Aline, astonished. "It seems strange that your father has not told you. There is no one he admires so much as Tegnér; but I daresay he is too modest to let his own children know of the relationship. Your paternal grand-father's mother and Tegnér's mother were sisters; so your grandfather and Tegnér were first cousins. That is why I thought you would have a leaning toward authorship."

Aline paused as if she expected an answer; but I was speechless. I tried to withdraw my hand from the muff, but she held it firmly.

"You know," she continued, "it is the most dangerous thing that can happen to a person to nourish an illusion that he is to become something out of the ordinary, if the necessary powers are lacking. Later, when it becomes evident that he has not the requisite talent, he usually becomes a misanthrope and a lamentable failure. It is easy to uproot such fancies when one is still a child, but afterward it is almost impossible."

Aline was serious. It was hard for her to tell me

what she felt she must say. I know that I have often talked freely with her about my desire to write stories, although at the time I did not take the matter very seriously. Therefore I didn't much mind what Aline had just said. But I asked her how she had found out that I had not the ability to become a writer.

"When I went away from here last autumn," she said, "it was partly for your sake; that you might have a teacher with more knowledge and experience than I have. I thought Elin would be just the teacher you needed. But Elin says she does not think there is anything exceptional about you. At least, there is no indication of it yet; she does not think you more gifted than the other children. You will be angry with me, I fear; but it is much better that you should know this now, before it is too late. Anyhow, you can become a fine woman."

I feel a little hurt, but it is not worth mentioning. For I have never really believed I have any talent for writing; and now that Elin thinks I have no unusual ability, I take the matter calmly.

"You are not crying, dear, are you?" says Aline. She speaks gently but her voice sounds troubled.

"No, dear Aline, I'm not crying. You are very kind to tell me this."

Aline is silent for a moment, after which she tells me that she is betrothed. I am so amazed that I

forget all she has said to me before. Then she informs
me that she is to marry a childhood friend whose
name is Adolf Arnell. He is the one she has loved all
her life, she says. She thought at times he had ceased
to care for her, but his seeming indifference was due
to the fact that his circumstances made it impossible
for him to marry. When she left Mårbacka, it had
been nearly over between them, but now all is well
again and she is very happy.

I rejoice in her happiness and am glad that she has
told me of this herself. I think she must have told
Mamma and Elin, but no one else, except me. Aline
probably knows that I am fonder of her than are
either Anna or Gerda. And so when we come back
from our stroll Aline and I are as fast friends as before
she went away.

After we remove our wraps, Aline steps into the
bedroom to speak to Mamma, but I go straight to
the kitchen bedroom, where Elin Laurell is sitting,
as usual, discoursing on predestination with Aunt
Lovisa.

"You think, then, Elin, that it's all a matter of
chance?" Auntie says.

"No," says Elin, "I don't believe it's merely a
matter of chance. I think that if a person really
makes up his mind to do a thing he can do it."

Although I had not been discouraged by what
Aline had told me, I feel thankful to Elin for what

she has said. Perhaps I can become a writer if it depends only on the will and not on talent. For will I think I have.

I feel attracted to Elin the moment she says that about the will. Drawing close to her side, I listen eagerly to everything she says. Without thinking, I lay a hand upon her shoulder. She turns her head toward me and smiles. And then I remember that I want to be loyal to Aline and not to like Elin; at least, I mean not to let her see that I do. Then it suddenly occurs to me that Aline no longer cares whether or not a little girl at Mårbacka likes her. Aline has a sweetheart now and is going to be married. So I am quite free to like Elin as much as I wish. And now I am just as good friends with Elin as ever I was with Aline, and even better perhaps.

XV
PASTOR UNGER

As we sit at the supper table Aline tells us a beautiful story about Pastor Unger. I am happy when I hear Papa and the others say that he has done a great thing, for I like Pastor Unger. Of all the gentlemen who come here to see Papa I think he is the kindest and most genial.

Pastor Unger always comes on a seventeenth of August, and at other times, too, when we have parties. But the remarkable thing is that he also comes on days when no one else would dare venture near the house.

We don't know how he manages to calculate the very day during the Christmas preparations when we are the busiest and the house is all upset. But when two maids are down on their knees scouring the floor in Papa's and Mamma's room, and all the furniture has been moved out into the front hall; when two hired charwomen are cleaning the parlour and have moved the furniture from there into the dining room; when Mamma is out in the kitchen, standing at one end of the pastry board making Yule cakes while the housekeeper stands at the other end making wort bread; when Aunt Lovisa has escaped to her room, where she and Anna and I are making small cakes; when Papa is sitting in the dining room walled in by the parlour furniture on one side and the furniture from the kitchen bedroom on the other—then we know that Pastor Unger is not far away.

As the pastor drives up in his little carriole we bewail that company should come on a day like this, and we tell Papa that he'll have to go out to receive the pastor, as the rest of us are not fit to be seen. But we don't wail nearly so loud or so long as we would had it been anyone else than Pastor Unger.

As soon as Papa has stepped out to the porch, he shouts to the pastor that he'd better drive on, for in this house there are only old charwomen and bake-women. But Pastor Unger, undaunted, hops down from his carriole and comes briskly up the steps.

"So you are busy house-cleaning, too?" he says. "I thought as much, for at our house Maria is up to her ears with cleaning and scouring; so she chased me out."

Then he follows Papa into the dining room. Papa sits down in his rocker, and Pastor Unger selects the worst chair he can find and draws it up to the rocking chair. Before he has had time to sit down, he is telling a funny story. The next moment he is out in the kitchen and in the bedroom beyond.

"I hear that Louise and Lovisa would not come in to shake hands with me; so I was obliged to come out to them."

If their hands just then are covered with dough, he gives them each a hearty pat on the shoulder that makes the flour dust fly around them. And he says to the housekeeper:

"I can see that your Christmas will be a failure, because your wort loaves are flat as pancakes." To which the housekeeper retorts:

"There must be something wrong with your eyes, since you can't see that they are round as a dean's belly."

Then he conveys greetings from Maria to Mamma and Aunt Lovisa, and, glancing about, he remarks: "All the womenfolk here look as if dressed for a party by comparison with those at home." After that he asks for a taste of the ginger cake, as there's nothing he enjoys more. He looks into the dough trough to see whether the dough is rising and goes over to the stove and lifts the lids off all the pots to see whether there is any decent food for dinner or if he must go elsewhere to dine. And last he picks up a whisk, and, dipping it into the flour jar, sprinkles

flour over us children. We are not slow to pay him
back. Taking the wooden spoons we use to mix the
dough for the small cakes, we pelt him with flour. A
wild battle ensues in the kitchen bedroom! Amid
shrieks and laughter the baking tins are swept off
the table and the fine white flour fills the air with
clouds of dust. Aunt Lovisa shouts above the din
that we should take the home-ground meal if we
want to waste it, and not the expensive flour from
the mill. Mamma comes in just then and drives
Pastor Unger out of the kitchen bedroom.

Mamma says, "I can understand why Maria has
to send Alfred away on a day like this. She can't have
a madcap like him around the house in the midst of
Christmas preparations."

"And to think that such a man should be a preacher!" the housekeeper mumbles, so that the pastor
won't hear her.

Before dinner we make ourselves a little more
presentable. Although we think it is a waste of pre-
cious time, I'm sure that both Mamma and Aunt
Lovisa are glad of a little break in the work.

Talking comes easy to Pastor Unger, and I love
to hear him talk. But Papa, who has been listening to
him for two hours, looks tired out. As Papa is never
quite well during the winter months, he is silent all
through dinner and lets Mamma and Aunt Lovisa
entertain the pastor.

As soon as we sit down to table, Pastor Unger declares that he will have to leave West Ämtervik, as his remuneration is too small to live upon. He has said the same thing every year at this time as far back as I can remember. So we children can hardly keep from laughing when he begins the same old story.

But Mamma says seriously: "We shall be sorry to lose so good a neighbour!" Then she asks him what pastorate he intends to seek.

Pastor Unger enumerates all the vacancies to be filled this year and also those that will occur the following year. Then, without Mamma's having to ask, he recounts the advantages and disadvantages of the various charges; the kind of living quarters they have and what remuneration is offered. He knows where the property is poor and where the forests have been cut down; where the stable is old and worm-eaten and where the rain comes in through the roof of the rectory. He is so entertaining that, whatever he says, it's a pleasure to listen. He is not only witty but also well informed. I learn so much from Pastor Unger!

After he has talked awhile about pastorates, livings, and rectories, he takes up the various clergymen who might apply for these places; what kind of clerical certificates they hold and how many years they have been in active service, how they preach and how they conduct their parish elections.

And I think it is just as interesting to hear about all these clergymen as about the different parsonages. I never tire of listening to *him*. I don't know what Mamma thinks, but at any rate she lets him talk on until the dessert is brought in. But when dinner is over she says:

"I cannot believe, Alfred, that you would move away from West Ämtervik."

"But I am forced to," he declares, with a gesture of helplessness. "The living is next to nothing. I assure you, Louise, that at times we haven't food for the day."

Mamma concedes that his salary is inadequate. "But I believe you are too much attached to West Ämtervik to abandon it. And think how well off Maria and you are since the parish built you a new rectory. There are few deans who have a more beautiful place to live in."

When Mamma speaks seriously like this, everyone listens, for she is not given to lengthy speeches.

"You say that the salary is too small," she continues. "But think of all the veal cutlets and all the pike and the cheese cakes and cubes of butter that are slipped into your kitchen. They also count for something."

"Yes, you are right," the pastor agrees.

"Maria and you have a marvellous facility for making your small income sufficient for all purposes. We don't know how you manage to do it. You and Pastor Lindegren at Halla have about the same living, but he has no horses or carriages such as you have, and his family cannot afford to entertain the best families, both of Ämtervik and Sunne, or give big parties, as they do at West Ämtervik."

After Mamma has preached to him in this strain awhile, Pastor Unger pushes aside his plate, and leaning back in his chair, he looks across the table with a slightly troubled expression.

"You are certainly right, Louise," he says. "I don't think I shall move before there is a vacancy at Gunnarskog. But I am obliged to seek that charge, as the Ungers have been pastors there for many generations, and I am known to everyone in the parish."

"Oh!" says Mamma. "Then let us hope that the rector at Gunnarskog may live for many years to come."

The autumn that Aline moved to West Ämtervik, Pastor Unger did not make his customary Christmas call, and now, while we are seated at the supper table, Papa wants to know how her uncle is.

"He isn't ill, is he?" says Papa. "He did not come last year while we were in the midst of the Christmas pother."

"No, he's not ill," Aline answers, "but he was greatly troubled just then. You know, of course, that the old rector of Gunnarskog died last autumn."

"Is Gunnarskog open?" Mamma exclaims. "In that case your uncle won't be long in West Ämtervik."

"Oh, yes, he will," Aline replies. She says it is true that her uncle had wished to go to Gunnarskog. He had spent his childhood there and knew everyone in the parish, and he thought the place a perfect paradise of beauty. He used to talk a good deal about rectories and livings; so one would have supposed that his only thought was to get a desirable pastorate. But Aline believed that even if he were offered one of the best livings, such as Sunne or Karlskoga, he would have preferred Gunnarskog.

"Then why does he not seek it?" asks Papa. "Is it for the sake of the people of West Ämtervik? Perhaps he feels that since they have put up a fine big rectory for him——"

No, Aline does not think so. Her uncle had told his parishioners a long time ago that as soon as Gunnarskog was open he intended to apply for the place. So they knew what to expect when they built the new rectory. But anyhow the people insisted on putting up a fine, spacious building for the help he had given them during the year of the famine.

"Aye, true!" says Papa. "I remember that he

raised a loan to buy seed corn for the sufferers and tried to procure some kind of gainful work for them. He has done quite as much for the people of West Ämtervik as they have done for him. He owes them nothing."

"But you see, Uncle Lagerlöf, the rector of Gunnarskog had been ill for many years and unable to attend to his pastoral duties. The last four years he had been obliged to have an assistant. The curate was an old post-horse (as it is called) of the Consistory. For many years he had had no fixed appointment. He is a poor man, with a wife and four children. Uncle Alfred thought that the curate had also hoped to have Gunnarskog, since he had served there for four years. Besides, he needs the place badly, as he has no home of his own but must board his wife and children at a farmhouse."

"Aye, that was a hard knot to unravel," Papa observes.

"Uncle talked about it every day," says Aline. "He wavered between desire and duty. Neither Aunt Maria nor I knew what he would decide. Gunnarskog drew him like a magnet, and yet he would not stand in the way of another clergyman, especially one who was old and poor.

"'Mustard is mixed with the honey,' he used to say. 'And the honey has lost its sweetness.' But all the same, he went to Karlstad the day before his application had to be in; so we concluded that he would apply for the charge."

"My dear," says Elin, "this is very interesting! How did it turn out?"

"The time limit was twelve o'clock," Aline continues, "and at eleven Uncle went into the chamber of the Consistory, where, it seems, they had been waiting for him all the morning. The moment he appeared, the registrar called out to him to hand over his credentials. But Uncle Alfred did not produce them. He sat down instead and began to chat, letting the time pass. At half-past eleven the registrar gave him another reminder.

"'Surely you are not thinking of letting this good living slip out of your hands, Alfred? You are not a young man, you know, and you can't afford to serve longer as perpetual curate.'

"'Oh, I am very well satisfied with West Ämtervik,' Uncle said, as if he had all the time in the world."

"What a man!" says Papa. "So he sat there with the credentials in his pocket and did not present them?"

"No, he did not present them," Aline answers. "When the clock struck the three-quarter hour the registrar became impatient. He reached over and felt of Uncle's breast pocket.

"'You have the documents with you,' he said. 'So out with them!' Uncle replied that he couldn't come to Karlstad with an empty purse. He sat there and talked, now of the new parsonage at West Ämtervik and of how contented his wife was there.

"'She'll be contented in Gunnarskog, too,' said the registrar. 'The whole parish wants you for its pastor.' He tried to talk Uncle into taking the pastorate of Gunnarskog, but to no avail. Thus the time passed until the clock began to strike the hour of twelve.

"Then Uncle Alfred arose from his chair and, thrusting his hand into his pocket, drew forth a packet of papers and showed the registrar that they contained his application for Gunnarskog. While the clock was striking he lowered his hand until the packet nearly touched the table, but he kept his hold on the papers. On the twelfth stroke, he slowly raised his hand and put the packet back in his pocket. Then, without a word, he put on his greatcoat and hat and walked out."

"What a man!" says Papa again.

"But you see, Uncle Lagerlöf, the hard part came afterward. The people of Gunnarskog had been so certain that Uncle Alfred would come that they had not looked for another clergyman. When they learned that he had not applied, they immediately wrote letters of inquiry and protest. Last week a large deputation came from Gunnarskog. They were the leading peasants of that parish—fine upstanding fellows, and Uncle knew them all. They told him that the parish wished to call him on probation. They assured him that he would get every vote if he would only accept the call. I heard how they pleaded and tried to talk him over. I tell you it was touching. Of course they did not beg him on their knees, but they pleaded as if for their lives: They were in great need of a capable clergyman. The last one had been sick so long that the parishioners had gone, as it were, astray. You can understand, Uncle Lagerlöf, how this would affect him. Just to see the familiar faces was a reminder of everything that he had loved; and, besides, to hear that they were in need of someone to guide them along the right path affected him even more. I can't understand how he could refuse."

"And was it all merely for the sake of that curate?" Elin asks.

"Yes. He had applied and must stand on the nomination list. Uncle Alfred thought if he did not accept the call, then perhaps the curate might be chosen. The Gunnarskog peasants tried to convince him that they didn't want the curate, but Uncle said he hoped they would change their minds. No, that they would never do, they declared. They had had an ailing rector long enough, and the curate was too old and sickly. If it was on his account that Uncle would not accept, he was making a useless sacrifice."

"And yet he refused?" asks Papa. I see the fine wrinkles around his eyes twitch in the way they always do when he tries to hold back the tears.

"Yes, Uncle Lagerlöf. But he did not sleep that night, after the Gunnarskog peasants had appealed to him. I could hear him pacing up and down his study all night long."

"Gad, what a man!" Papa exclaims once again.

Aunt Lovisa thinks they ought to make him a bishop, to which we all jubilantly shout "Yes." We are simply elated because someone we know has done a great thing.

"I am not sorry he did it," Aline says to me when we are out walking after dinner. And I think if I could do something like that it would be far greater than to write the most wonderful book in the world.

But after I went to sleep that night I dreamed that I was trying to write something beautiful about Pastor Unger. And just as I had worked myself up to it and was writing at fever heat, Aunt Maria Unger came in; she said I had better stop, for writing was not my forte—everyone had said so.

When she told me this I thought I should die of grief, and when I awoke my face was wet with tears. I soon realized, however, that it was only a dream;

but my heart throbbed violently for what seemed like hours to me.

I cannot understand why the heart should ache so because Aunt Maria Unger said that to me in a dream. It did not trouble me at all when Aline talked to me in the same way when I was awake.

I turn over on my right side and then on my left; I press my hands against my heart, but it still pains me. At last I say to my heart that it mustn't feel so bad, for I am going to write books when I grow up, no matter what anyone says to discourage me.

After I talk to my heart awhile, it becomes quieter and stops aching. Then I go to sleep again.

Next morning I say to myself as I lie abed half awake: "I shall write novels when I am grown; for that is why I was born."

And I feel relieved and happy to know that this is settled. Before Aline had advised me not to write, I had felt only a vague, intangible longing, but now this longing has become a fixed determination.

XVI
THE EASTER WITCH

In the middle of the afternoon of Easter Eve two maids always steal out of the kitchen, each with a bundle of clothing under her arm, and go down to the cow barn. They do it as secretly as possible, so that we children won't notice anything unusual. But we know, all the same, that they are going to make up an Easter witch, because Nurse Maja has told us all about it.

Down there in the cow barn they hunt up a long narrow sack and stuff it with straw. That done, they dress the sack in a soiled and ragged old skirt and jacket, the poorest they can find—one that is threadbare and out at the elbows into the bargain. The sleeves of the jacket they also fill with straw, to make the arms look natural and plump. For the hands, they pull some straw below the sleeves.

After that the maids make a head for the Easter

witch of a coarse grey kitchen towel, tied together at the four corners, and fill it, too, with straw. They sketch the eyes, nose, mouth, and two or three wisps of hair with charcoal; and then top the head with an old screen bonnet which the housekeeper puts on in summer when she is going to capture a swarm of bees.

When the witch is ready, the maids carry her up to the house. They dare not bring her inside, however, but stop at the foot of the steps leading to the porch. They fetch a kitchen chair in which they set her down, and then run over to the brew house for the long oven rake and the broom and place them at the back of the chair; for if the witch has not the oven rake and broom with her, no one will know she is a witch. They also bind securely to her apronstrings a muddy cow horn filled with magic oil, such as witches use when they ride to *Blåkulla*, the Witches' Kitchen. In the horn they stick a long feather, and, last, they hang an old post bag round her neck.

Then the maids go into the kitchen, and the housekeeper comes up to the nursery to tell us children that one of those horrid witches who ride on a broomstick every Easter Eve has dropped down in the yard at Mårbacka. "She is sitting just outside the entrance," says the housekeeper, "and a hideous-looking creature she is! So you children had better stay in the house until she's gone."

But we know what is going to happen and rush

past the housekeeper and down the steps to see the Easter witch. Papa of course comes with us; but Mamma and Aunt Lovisa say they prefer to remain inside, as they have seen so many Easter witches in their time.

Coming out on the porch to look for the witch, we see her sitting below, glaring up at us with her coal-black eyes. We pretend to be awfully frightened, and that we think she is really and truly a witch, on her way to the Blåkulla. We know, of course, that she is only a straw witch, but we are supposed to be frightened—that is part of the play. Otherwise, the maids who have gone to the trouble of making the effigy for us would have nothing for their pains.

When we have gazed at the Easter witch awhile from a safe distance, we creep cautiously down the steps. She holds herself rigidly erect as we approach, until at last one of us thrusts a hand into the bag. The old, discarded post bag is bulging with mail, and we keep a watchful eye on it the whole time. But the one who is the first to thrust a hand into the bag lets out a wild shriek of delight, for the bag is filled with letters.

We take out great handfuls of fat letters, all bearing seals, to each of which is attached a wing feather —as though they had flown hither. All the letters are for Johan and Anna and Gerda and me. The grown-ups get none.

As soon as we have gathered them up, we go into the house and sit down at the dining-room table to open our Easter letters. It is heaps of fun; for Easter letters are seldom written with pen and ink but are painted. In the middle of the page of every letter stands a gay-coloured Easter man or Easter woman holding a broom, a rake, a horn, and the other Pascal implements.

We receive many kinds of letters. Some are mere daubs done by small children, while others are in black ink like the usual letter; but always in the middle of the page stands the Old Easter Man or the Old Easter Woman done in colours. It is evident that the grown-ups have helped the children with some of the drawings; for they are not all done equally well, but we don't care. The important thing is to get many letters so we can boast about them when we go to church on Easter Sunday and meet our cousins from Gårdsjö.

As a matter of fact it is not strictly true that there is no writing in these Easter letters, for some are covered with verse. We don't get much pleasure out of these verses, as they are merely old Easter rhymes which come year after year and which we already know by heart.

We always pretend to be surprised that the flying witch has brought us so many letters, although we expected them. We ourselves have devoted every spare moment, during the month of March, to drawing and painting, and have sent out our Easter letters to every manor house in this part of the country. So we know they have worked in the same way at the other manor houses and that the letters the Easter witch has brought have come from Gårdsjö, from Herrestad, from Visteberg and other manors.

When we have gone over our letters and figured out who has sent them, we remember the Easter witch and run out to the porch to have another look at her.

But now the chair is vacant; the witch has flown and taken the oven rake and broom with her. She must have been in a hurry to get to the Witches' Kitchen and flown off as soon as she had delivered the Easter post.

"It is lucky for her that she escaped," we say with a laugh, "for here comes Per of Berlin! Per is a Finn, with hunter's blood in his veins." He has just stepped out of the office, where he has loaded two of Papa's shotguns. Taking his stand on the flagstone in front of the office, he fires the shots into the air. We know, of course, that he's shooting at the Easter witches although we cannot see them. But Per of Berlin, being a Finn, sees more than the rest of us and must know what he is doing.

This year we have painted many more Easter letters than usual. Elin Laurell is not so strict about our lessons as Aline used to be, therefore we have had more time to ourselves. The nursery at Mårbacka has been turned into a regular workshop with colours and mixing cups all over the room. The busiest time was during Holy Week, when Elin was in Karlstad visiting relatives. Papa was in despair because we had begged from him all his fine white linen paper. Finally he said that we'd have to be satisfied now with common yellow straw paper, as that was all he had left. The pretty red and blue colours with which we all love to paint had given out; so we had to run down to Aunt Lovisa and borrow the box of fine colours she had saved from her boarding school days at Åmål. All the drinking glasses in the nursery were taken to wash our brushes in, and we used up every stick of sealing wax in the house. Mamma sat addressing letters days on end, and we ran about in every lane searching for pretty feathers to attach to the envelope with a seal. There was always a dearth of brushes, and when the last letter had been sealed, nothing was left of them but a few thin wisps of hair.

We are so glad that Easter Eve has come at last and we are through with the painting! If we receive as many letters in return as we sent out, it will take more than one Easter witch to deliver them.

In the late afternoon the housekeeper comes again to tell us that another dreadful witch is sitting below the porch, and to warn us children to stay indoors until she has gone. But we run down from the nursery at once to look at her. Papa, as usual, goes with us, and, for a change, Mamma and Aunt Lovisa come, too, and even Uncle Wachenfeldt, who is spending the Easter holidays with us, comes limping out to the porch.

It is cold outside, and windy; so the Easter witch can't have had any too pleasant a journey. We pretend, as usual, that we are afraid of her and steal down the steps softly and with the utmost caution.

This Easter witch is exactly like the other one; so we are not really and truly frightened at sight of her, though we pretend to be. The straw sticks out below the sleeves of the jacket as on all Easter witches. The eyes, nose, and mouth, and two or three wisps of hair have been sketched with charcoal on a grey kitchen towel, the dairymaid's shawl is spread across the shoulders, the old, soiled post bag hangs round the neck, and tied to the apronstrings is the filthy cow horn.

This time I am the first to thrust my hand into the post bag, but I have barely touched the letters when the sorceress jumps up. She quickly takes out the feather from the cow horn and smears my face with the witches' salve.

But how can this be? What does it mean? I cry out in terror as I rush toward the porch. But the straw woman can run, too, and is after me, hotfoot, to smear me again with the witches' oil.

Not only am I frightened, but I am also baffled by the strange sight of an Easter witch who can move. When she sprang up from the chair, anxious and perplexing thoughts ran through my mind. If an old stuffed sack can come to life, the dead, too, can rise from their graves, and wicked trolls are to be found in the woods. Then there is nothing too horrible or too uncanny to be true.

I run shrieking up the steps to the veranda. If I can only get to where the grown folks are, they will protect me. Anna, Gerda, and Johan rush past me in the same direction. They are as frightened as I am. But the grown-ups are standing on the porch, laughing.

"Dear children," they say, "there's nothing to be afraid of—it's only Nurse Maja!"

Then we understand, of course, how stupid we have been. We might have known it was Nurse Maja dressed up as an Easter witch. How provoking that we have let ourselves be so scared! And, most of all, it is provoking to one who, for several years, has practised at being brave.

But this is no time to stand here blaming ourselves or others; for now the Easter witch, with arms outstretched, comes rushing up the steps, making straight for Uncle Wachenfeldt to embrace and kiss him. And Uncle Wachenfeldt, who abhors all ugly women, spits and curses and fends her off with his cane. But I'm not so sure that he escapes her onslaught, for there are two black smudges on his white moustaches.

The Easter witch, not content with that, gives him a poke with the oven rake and then rides off toward the kitchen. The pigeons, which are so tame they eat out of your hand and are not easily scared, take to their wings at sight of her, and the cat leaps on to the eaves trough, while Nero, the dog, who is big as a bear, slinks out of her way, with his tail between his legs. But the old housekeeper is not afraid. Quick as a flash, she runs over to the stove, seizes the steaming coffee pot, and goes straight up to the ogress the moment she appears on the threshold.

And when the Easter witch sees the raised coffee pot, she turns and flees in the direction of the barnyard, riding like mad on her broomstick. The first to see her is the old bay mare. She has just been unharnessed and is walking calmly toward the door of the stable, when the face of a scarecrow looms up before her. Without stopping to reflect, she doubles her legs against her belly and sets off, her mane flying, her tail standing straight out, her hoofs beating the earth—running wild till her way is barred by a high fence.

Lars of London and Magnus of Vienna, who are down by the shed cutting firewood, pause in their

work when they see her. It would not do for sturdy
fellows like them to flee at sight of a witch. Without
moving from the spot, they raise their axes against
her, knowing that witches are afraid of steel. Nor
does the Easter witch dare to approach them.

Just then she sees a man coming down the avenue.
Strangely enough, the man is Olle of Maggebysäter,
who once in his youth came upon a band of Easter
witches. While going home from a party one Easter
Eve, on a meadow below Mårbacka, he saw them
sweep across the field in a long procession. They
wound themselves around him, like a snare. Then
they danced with him all night, over a newly ploughed
field, never letting him stop for a moment to take
breath. He had thought then the witches would dance
the life out of him; and now, as he comes to the servants' hall at Mårbacka, he sees just such a witch as
he had seen in his youth come riding toward him on
a broomstick.

He does not wait for her to come very close. Old
and crippled with rheumatism as he is, he turns
abruptly and runs down the avenue as swiftly as a
boy, never stopping until he has reached the woods
on the other side of the road.

Now that we children are over our fright, we can
laugh at the others as we follow at the heels of the
Easter witch. We have seen the housekeeper threaten
her with the steaming hot coffee, seen the horse shy

and Olle of Maggebysäter take to the woods. We have also seen Lars of London and Magnus of Vienna raise their axes at her. I don't think we have ever laughed so much in our lives!

But the best of all is when Per of Berlin comes running past the porch toward the office. Papa asks him where he is hurrying to. The old man scarcely takes time to answer. But at last it comes out: He is going to load the shotguns again and shoot dead the horrible creature who runs about in the yard.

And anyone can see that the zest of the chase is in his eyes. For old Per of Berlin has been gunning for Easter witches these fifty years and has never caught a single one. But here at last is a witch he can catch on the run.

XVII
ANNA LAGERLÖF

I DON'T understand why Anna should always be saying that she knows she is going to be unhappy—she who is so pretty, so wise, and so well beloved!

It would be more fitting that I, who am ugly and lame, should talk that way. But such a thought never enters my head. For, so long as there are interesting books to read, it seems to me that neither I nor anyone else, for that matter, need be unhappy.

This spring a friend loaned us the *Barber-Surgeon's Tales* by Topelius, and in the evening someone reads aloud from the book while we sit round the lamp working. With such a fascinating book to read, I don't see how Anna can think of sorrow and misfortune.

Sometimes Anna stands before the picture of a churchyard, made by Aunt Anna Wachenfeldt, which hangs in Aunt Lovisa's room. After gazing at the picture awhile, she always says that she knows she will be as unhappy as Aunt Anna.

I do not like to hear her say this, and ask her how she can be so sure of that. "Because," she replies, "everyone who bears the name of Anna Lagerlöf is unlucky."

I think this most extraordinary in Anna, who is usually such a sensible girl. Even if Aunt Anna did grieve herself to death, that is no reason why everyone whose name is Anna Lagerlöf should have a similar fate.

Anna is to be confirmed this year and is receiving instruction from Pastor Lindegren. She has become very quiet and meek of late, as if her thoughts were far away. Nor does she make so many remarks as usual about Gerda and me. She helps us get ready when we are going away and sees that we are properly dressed and our hair nicely combed. But this she has always done, only now it seems to be no trouble to her; she does it as though she loved us.

The house has become so peaceful since Anna has been preparing for Confirmation. Gerda and I do not shriek or sing now at the top of our lungs. No one has forbidden us, but we think it isn't fitting at this time.

There has been so much discord in the kitchen this year. The housekeeper is growing old and cranky, and the maids no longer respect her authority. They

answer her impudently when she gives orders, or
flatly refuse to do her bidding. Then she scolds them
and they talk back. It is very unpleasant. But when
Anna passes through the kitchen they all become
quiet. For the maids cannot quarrel with the housekeeper when they see Anna.

The moment Anna enters a room everyone is aware
that she is a little girl preparing for Confirmation.
I can't say just what there is about her, but nevertheless I know this is true.

Nurse Maja says that old man Per of Berlin has
told her that if he were a dog he couldn't bark when
that girl passed by.

We know that Mamma has always thought more of
Anna than of her other children. And no wonder!
Anna has been more helpful to Mamma than we
have been. Gerda wants only to play, and I want
to read, but Anna, like Mamma, loves to hem a bit
of linen or mend a ragged garment. And now that
Anna is reading for Confirmation, it seems as if
Mamma were going to be confirmed, too; for she sits
studying the Bible and the catechism, just like Anna.
And she does this on a weekday—she who is always
so busy sewing that she hasn't time to open a book,
except on Sunday.

The other day I came upon Papa reading Tegnér's
Children of the Lord's Supper. And now Mamma
tells us that it won't do to read any more of the

Barber-Surgeon's Tales at present, because they might draw Anna's thoughts away from preparing for her First Communion. Mamma doesn't mean that there is anything bad about the book, but she thinks it might fill the girl's mind with a lot of worldly thoughts. Although I am pretty sure that the two dapper Counts Bertelsköld cannot take Anna's thoughts away from her reading, we do as Mamma wishes.

Hilda Wallroth and Emilie Nilsson also are being prepared this year for Confirmation by Pastor Lindegren. They, too, are carried away, as it were. And when the three are together they are so solemn you hardly know what to say to them.

The children of East Ämtervik have always dressed in black at their First Communion. But Fru Lindegren thinks that the three girls from the manors should wear white when they partake of the Lord's Supper. She says it's a pity that the dear little children should go up to the altar in heavy and unbecoming black woollen frocks. Happily, Fru Lindegren persuaded Mamma and Papa, Uncle Kalle and Aunt Augusta, and Herr and Fru Nilsson to depart from the old custom and let Anna, Hilda, and Emilie be confirmed in white.

On the drive to the church, Mamma sits with Anna on the back seat of the drosky. Gerda and I, as usual, sit with our backs to the horses. But today I am not sorry to ride backward, for in this way I can look at Anna the whole time.

But it is not at her dress I am looking, nor at the filigree brooch she received from Mamma as a Confirmation gift. I am looking into her eyes.

They are large soulful eyes of a greyish-brown, with perhaps a tinge of olive. However, it is not their color that I see, but their expression of serene expectancy. I should love to know what it is that she expects. It seems to me as though she were standing outside the iron gate of some great and glorious castle and longing to be let in to see the beautiful rooms, the broad staircases, and the vaulted ceilings.

Somehow I feel certain that her wish will be granted. Before long the gate will open and a handsome young prince, dressed in satin and velvet, will come out and bow low to Anna, saying that he is Count Bernhard Bertelsköld and bid her welcome to Majniemi Castle.

But Anna will not look at him or take his proffered hand, nor will she pass through the gate; for Anna does not stand outside Majniemi Castle; she stands at the gate of heaven waiting to see God and His angels.

When we arrive at the church, Adolf Noreen hurries forward to open the drosky door and help us out. I can see by the way he looks at Anna that he thinks she is lovely in her white frock and filigree brooch.

But Anna is not aware of his presence. Her gaze is fixed on something far, far away.

As Anna and Hilda and Emilie walk up the chancel in their white dresses, a gasp of astonishment is heard throughout the church. The people crane their necks to catch a glimpse of them. One young man actually stands up in the pew to get a better view. But he is promptly told by those nearest him to sit down.

Today I can hear every word Pastor Lindegren says, for Mamma, Aunt Lovisa, Gerda, and I are seated in the nave, close behind the children who are to take their First Communion. And the pastor talks to the children in a way that makes them long for the gates of heaven to open.

A few days later Nurse Maja tells me—but perhaps I should not call her Nurse Maja now, for she has been promoted to the position of parlourmaid—that when Anna came to church in her white dress and her Confirmation brooch, she looked so lovely that a boy in the Confirmation class fell madly in love with her. "He knew he could never have her," says Maja, "therefore he did not want to stay in East Ämtervik any longer, and was going to sail for America in the autumn."

Nurse Maja also tells me that he wrote a poem in which he said that because of his love for Anna he must go far away. The poem is so beautiful, she says, that all the children in the Confirmation class copied it, to keep as a remembrance. Maja has a copy, too, which she will let me see if I promise not to show it to Mamma or Papa or to Anna herself. For if I did, the boy would be so furious at Nurse Maja that he might kill her.

All that the maid has told me sounds so grand that I beg her by all means to let me read the love poem the poor lad wrote to Anna. But after reading it, I feel a bit disappointed. The poem contains only five lines, and there is nothing in it about Anna:

My name is Erik Persson, my home is Karlstad Parish,
When the flower withers I shall go away.
Farewell, my father and my mother,
Farewell, my sister and my brother,
And thou, oh, my white-clad girl!

"But, Maja, there is nothing in it about his love for Anna!"

"But doesn't he say 'my white-clad girl'? What more do you want?"

Well, perhaps it's enough. Anyhow, Nurse Maja may be sure that I shall not show the verse to Anna. For the day that Anna partook of the Lord's Supper is to her so sacred that it would never do to mention any earthly love in connection with that day.

XVIII
UNCLE SCHENSON

UNCLE SCHENSON had been married to Aunt Johanna Wallroth, who was Mamma's sister and also a sister to Aunt Georgina and Aunt Julia; but Aunt Johanna died so long ago that we children scarcely remember her.

Although our maternal aunt is dead, Uncle Schenson still visits us every summer, just as Uncle Wachenfeldt, who had married our paternal aunt Anna, comes every year at Christmas and at Easter.

Uncle Schenson is headmaster of a boys' school in Karlstad, and the day after the spring term is over he comes to Mårbacka, and the day before school is to open again, in the autumn, he goes back to Karlstad. He always brings us a big bagful of nuts, which we children love. But Aunt Lovisa gets so angry when she hears him rattle the nuts in the bag, for she has such poor teeth that she can't chew nuts.

"It's most extraordinary about that man Schenson," she declares. "There's Yhnell's confectionery shop at Karlstad, which is the best in the world, yet he comes bringing the kind of stuff no one can eat."

That is the only thing about Uncle Schenson, however, which Aunt Lovisa disapproves.

Uncle Schenson is not a fussy guest, and he is sure that he puts us to no extra trouble. He is satisfied with the kind of fare we set before him; but while he is here we serve *hors d'œuvres* with every meal and dessert several times a week. It wouldn't do to offer him dry rusks with his afternoon coffee; there must be small cakes and pastry, also. If in the evening we neglected to set cognac and cold water before him, so that he could mix a grog for himself, he would think we were tired of him and take it as a hint that we wished he would go.

Uncle Schenson appreciates the privilege of spending his summers at Mårbacka and makes himself useful from the first day to the last. After breakfast he goes the rounds of the farm with Papa: first to the stable, then to the byre, and then out to the labourers in the fields. When, in this way, he has helped Papa with his many duties, if he happens to see Aunt Lovisa sitting on the steps hulling berries or shelling peas, he immediately goes over to her and offers to help. It is no fault of his that she would rather do the work herself. But, she adds, if he would sit down

awhile and tell her something about the grand parties
at the bishop's or the governor's he has attended
during the winter, the work would go ever so much
faster. And when he has lightened Auntie's duties
in this way, he looks up Daniel and Johan and takes
them along with him to Gårdsjö for a dip in the lake.
It is a half-hour's walk to the lake, uphill and muddy
all the way. I hardly think the boys would bother
to go if Uncle Schenson did not take them along.
When they return from their bath, about one o'clock,
he feels that he has earned his dinner.

After dinner Uncle Schenson and Papa go down to
the office for their midday nap. And later, when
afternoon coffee has been served, he reads aloud to
Mamma and Aunt Lovisa or anyone else who will
listen. As he is a large, corpulent man he reads slowly,
clearing his throat every little while. I think it must
be a strain on him to read aloud; but he wants to be
of use to us and not a burden.

After the reading, when Uncle has had his grog,
he goes for a stroll with Anna, Gerda, and me. But
Uncle Schenson does not go merely for the pleasure
of our company, but because he wants to protect
us in case we should meet any vicious cows or bulls
grazing in the meadow. We know that he is terribly
afraid of bulls and cows; so we understand how kind
it is of him to come with us.

On the Sundays that we do not attend church, and

Uncle Schenson, as well as the rest of us, would like to lie on the grass and read an entertaining story, he always reads to us the service for the day. I am sure it is a sacrifice on his part, but he doubtless regards it as a duty to hold us to some form of piety.

If Uncle Schenson thought he was a trouble to us rather than a help he would never come to Mårbacka; for he is a very considerate and tender-hearted man.

We have to be guarded in our speech when Uncle is here. For if we say of a person that he is ugly or untruthful or stingy, Uncle Schenson gets all stirred up about it. "You must not say such things about your neighbours," he tells us, and points a warning finger.

We always say that Uncle should have been a priest so he could teach people how to be good. We cannot understand why he should teach only algebra and Euclid.

If Uncle Schenson is out driving, when he comes to a hill he always gets out so as to spare the horse. Papa and the stableman, or anyone else who happens to be along, remain seated in the carriage; but not Uncle Schenson!

And if he attends a dinner party he looks to see if there is not some tubby widow or elderly spinster whom no one cares to talk to, and sits down beside her. He always knows what to say to such poor neglected old ladies. As Uncle Schenson is a big fat man, I'm sure that he does not care to dance. But if he attends a party where there is dancing, and sees some lady whom nobody else invites to dance, he immediately comes forward and offers her his arm. He waltzes carefully and slowly one or two rounds. Folks laugh a little, but at the same time they can't help but admire his chivalry.

He has a little home of his own in Karlstad, where he lives with his family. The house is beautifully situated on the bank of a river. We always stop there when we have an errand in the city. Uncle meets us at the railway station and takes us to the train when we leave. He buys our tickets and also presents us with a pound of sweets as we part. Those sweets he never forgets.

Once, when Mamma took me to a school commencement at Karlstad, we stopped, as usual, with Uncle Schenson. I remember how comfortable and cozy his home was. I saw then what a thoughtful and kindly man he was. He had his mother—a feeble old lady who was bed-ridden—living with him, also his sister Matilda, who acted as head of his household, and two dependent cousins. But Aunt Matilda and the cousins made themselves useful; so perhaps it was not wholly out of charity that he had taken them in. And he also had another sister who lived with him.

Uncle Schenson had three children, Ernst, Klaës,

and Alma, whose rooms were abovestairs in the little house. Once, when I was going up to Alma's room, I saw a face peering down over the banister. It was not the face of anyone I knew or expected to find in that house. I stood aghast as I saw the mysterious figure raise a threatening hand at me. The eyes flashed as though they emitted sparks of fire. A moment later I saw a wraithlike form disappear in the darkness of the garret.

I thought it might be a ghost I had seen. But I said nothing about it until Mamma and I were on our way home. And then Mamma told me that the person I had seen was a sister of Uncle Schenson's who was not in her right mind. She was not dangerous, Mamma explained, but she shunned people. I thought it so kind of Uncle Schenson to take his poor demented sister into his home!

Sometimes Mamma tells us a little about our Aunt Johanna, who had been married to Uncle Schenson. She was very beautiful and not at all like other girls. Grandmother had much anxiety on her account. She loved above everything to drive and tend horses. When she was a child she had a billy goat she used to drive all over Filipstad.

Johanna was not a shy child nor was she afraid. She would chat with the farmers who stood in the marketplace selling their produce, and sometimes they let her ride with them out of the city. Grand-

father often had to send the servants out into the
highways and byways to search for her. She made
friends with all the rough iron-ore haulers who lived
on Grandfather's estate. Grannie was horrified when
she saw her daughter sitting in a sledge in the company of a lot of half-intoxicated fellows, sharing their
coarse bread and bacon.

It was impossible for Aunt Johanna to accustom
herself to women's work of any sort, but she was all
the more capable when allowed to help in Grandfather's general store. "If only she had been a boy,"
said Mamma, "and could have stood behind a
counter selling herring or syrup, she would have been
happy." But being a girl, she was a constant source
of anxiety to her parents.

Grandfather and Grandmother once sent her to a
boarding school at Södertälje. While there she made
a Swiss landscape of stones, moss, and bits of looking-
glass, which was about all she had achieved. When
the picture was finished she ran away. Nothing could
induce her to go back to the school. All one learned
there, she declared, was to crib and lie, and she
wouldn't stand for that.

When we heard that Aunt Johanna was so self-
willed and daring we wondered how she came to
marry Uncle Schenson—he who is always so cour-
teous and so dignified and so careful of what he says
about others. We have often asked Mamma how

those two happened to marry; but that is something she will not tell.

We do not know for certain, but we think Uncle Schenson and Aunt Johanna were not happy together. They were too unlike one another in every way. But what we do know is that Aunt Johanna loved to tend and drive horses, even after her marriage.

Uncle Kalle of Gårdsjö had a stallion called Flyer, which he used to drive when he went out alone. The horse was so wild that no one would venture out with him when he drove that animal. Aunt Johanna was the only one, except Uncle Kalle himself, who dared ride behind Flyer.

Once when Uncle Kalle had driven Flyer into Karlstad, Aunt Johanna asked him if she might borrow the stallion, as she wished to go for a drive. She invited Aunt Nana Hammargren, who lived in Karlstad at the time, to go with her. That drive Aunt Nana will remember as long as she lives!

Flyer set off at a mad gallop. It seemed as if his hoofs hardly touched the ground; his eyes flashed fire, while the ice he kicked up in the road flew in their faces like a shower of needles. Aunt Nana feared the horse was running away, and said she never expected to get home alive, but Aunt Johanna held a slack rein—you could not hold Flyer in or he would kick over the traces. Johanna was enjoying the drive hugely.

"Isn't it great, Nana?" she said. "Flyer is my life! Did you ever see a horse to match him?"

But if Uncle Schenson and Aunt Johanna loved one another we'll never know. Just now we children are wondering if Uncle Schenson is going to marry Aunt Lovisa. We know that he has had his eye on her for several years, and now that his mother is dead and one of his cousins has gone to America, perhaps he feels that, with a little more room in his house and not so many dependent upon him, he can afford to marry.

And we are not so sure that Aunt Lovisa herself has not some thought in that direction. At all events, she goes to a lot of extra trouble to prepare good meals for him. Aunt Lovisa and Uncle Schenson ought to be well suited to one another, for they both like life and gaiety around them while they themselves sit quietly by. And think how many grand parties Aunt Lovisa would give, to which she would invite both the bishop and the governor! And think how many parties they would attend! She would never again find time to sit and ponder on things that are sad.

And think how pleasant it would be for her to be called "Fru" and to be served at the same time as the elderly matrons when attending a dinner, instead of having to wait, as she must now, until all the young matrons have been served!

And think how attentive Uncle Schenson would be to her and how carefully he would drive when they went on a journey, and what steady and reliable old horses they would pick out for themselves when they came to the posting stations!

Aunt Lovisa would have preferred a clergyman, but Uncle Schenson is almost as good as ordained. He is clean-shaven and goes to church every Sunday, and all the clergymen in the diocese meet at his house when they come to Karlstad.

We cannot imagine any two who are better suited to one another than Uncle Schenson and Aunt Lovisa; and we believe Mamma and Papa think the same. We are curious to know how it will turn out.

Alma Schenson has been at Gårdsjö all summer, but is now at Mårbacka, spending a few days with her father. Alma is only eleven years old and full of life. She is used to wrestling with boys, for she has two brothers at home, besides a number of schoolboys who board with Uncle. Small as she is, it seems strange that all boys like her. They never leave her in peace, and at times they tease her until she cries; but, all the same, I think they must like her a lot.

But Alma doesn't care at all for boys; she likes no one but her papa. It must be because her mother

is dead that she is so fond of her father. She loves to
sit in his lap and stroke his hand. He does not have to
say a word to her; for she is happy just to be near
him.

We love our papa and think he is the best papa in
the world, but in a different way. Why, Alma would
die if her father did not love her! If she thought there
was someone he preferred to her, she would hate that
person and would want to kill her. I don't believe
Alma would tolerate a stepmother, no matter how
kind she was. She would be afraid that Uncle Schenson might think more of the stepmother than he
thought of her. We talk to her about everything else,
but avoid all mention of Uncle Schenson's and Aunt
Lovisa's courtship. We think it best that Uncle
should tell her of this himself.

But once, in the nursery, when Maja was helping
Alma arrange her hair, Maja asked how Alma would
like to have a stepmother. Alma sprang up. Jerking
her hair out of Maja's hands, she faced her.

"What kind of talk is that?" she demanded in a
harsh, strident voice, not at all like her usual one.
We were startled.

Maja was actually frightened. "Well, perhaps
there's nothing to it," she hastened to say. "It's only
the sort of thing that folks imagine."

But Alma went on questioning her. "Do you mean
Aunt Lovisa?"

"A kinder stepmother you could never have," said Maja, trying to mollify her.

But there was no mollifying Alma when there was talk of a stepmother. She picked up a knife from the table (it was only an ink eraser) and brandished it in Nurse Maja's face.

"Papa can marry Aunt Lovisa if he wants to," she said; "but he knows what will happen if he does."

Alma has lovely deep blue eyes and long black lashes which everyone admires. As she stood there brandishing the knife in front of Nurse Maja, I noted a curious thing: There was the same look in her eyes I had seen in those of her insane aunt.

"You're not going to stab anyone, are you?" asked Maja.

"No," said Alma. "I won't do that, but I'll drown myself if Papa marries again, and he knows it."

Although Alma is only a child, she means this seriously. And we understand, now, that it would never do for Uncle Schenson to marry. For were he to do so, his dear little daughter would go mad, just like his sister

After Alma went back to Gårdsjö, we noticed that he was less attentive to Aunt Lovisa, and that she did not prepare quite so many dainty dishes for him. Otherwise, as far as we children could see, everything was exactly as before.

XIX
THE POND

ALTHOUGH I am now thirteen years old I remember well the old duck pond we had at Mårbacka when we were little.

It was a small round pond. In summer it was black with tadpoles, and in the autumn it was covered with a green scum which, happily, hid the tadpoles from sight. The water in the pond was so muddy that it could not be used for washing clothes. Nor could one bathe in it on account of the quantities of horse leeches that abounded there. If a person were to get one of these horse leeches on him it would not let go until it had sucked all the blood out of his body. The housekeeper says they are more dangerous than the big leeches she keeps in a water bottle on the kitchen windowsill to draw out the blood from a swollen cheek caused by an aching tooth.

I remember that we had small joy of that pond

while open, but when it froze over, in the late autumn, it was another matter. The morning that Nurse Maja informed us that the ice was firm we hardly took time to get into our clothes before we were off. Papa went with us in order to test the ice with his cane, to make sure it was solid. We brought down from the garret all our old skates and ran over to the stable-man to have him grind them and put new straps where they were needed.

We were awfully keen about skating when we were little, and the fact that we had only a small pond to skate on didn't trouble us in the least. Toward Christmas, when the snow began to fall, we had a lot of bother keeping the ice clear. We shovelled and swept until the thirteen-day blizzard, when we had to give up skating and take to coasting instead.

Sometimes folks would say to Papa they thought it strange that he, who was such a lover of beauty, did not ditch out the duck pond. It was of no use to any-one, they said, and might even be a menace to health because of the horrible stench that arose therefrom on hot summer days. And, besides, it lay close to the road, in plain sight of everyone who came to Mår-backa. Even Aunt Lovisa, who otherwise clung faithfully to everything old, told Papa, time and time again, that the pond spoiled the looks of the whole place.

Whenever there was mention of doing away with

the duck pond we children became dreadfully
alarmed. For we didn't mind the tadpoles in spring
or the stale odor in summer; we thought only of the
skating. I must say there were not so many pleasures
one could have in November and December; so we
really needed the pond to skate on.

It was a long time before Papa did anything about
the duck pond. He built the new barn and laid out
the new garden, but the pond remained unchanged.
We children naturally thought it was for our sakes
that he refrained from ditching out the pond; for we
were the only ones who had any joy of it.

Then came a summer when Sven of Paris and
Magnus of Vienna began to work down by the duck
pond; so we understood that Papa had been obliged
to yield to the wishes of Aunt Lovisa and the others
who wanted to be rid of it.

Still we couldn't make out just what Sven of Paris
and Magnus of Vienna were doing. They had hauled
stone and gravel with which they were building a wall
—not right around the duck pond, but at a short
distance from it. What on earth was that wall for? we
wondered.

At all events it became clear to us that there would
be no more skating. I remember that we children
said among ourselves that it was awfully mean of
Aunt Lovisa to make Papa do away with the pond
and that Papa didn't care so much for us as we

thought, or he wouldn't have had the heart to deprive us of our greatest pleasure.

We asked Sven of Paris and Magnus of Vienna why they were putting up the wall, and they said that it was being built for the purpose of doing away with the old mud hole which held nothing but frogs and horse leeches.

We could hardly look at the wall, but despite our prayers, it grew from day to day, till at last it was finished. Then Sven of Paris and Magnus of Vienna cleared away the sod around the pond, and when that was done, they were ready to begin the ditching.

One morning, as we got out of bed, we saw all the grown-ups—Papa, Mamma, Aunt Lovisa, Uncle Schenson, and the housekeeper—go down to the duck pond. We knew then that the ditching was about to begin. We were so furious with the whole proceeding that we wouldn't even look at what they were doing. But curiosity must have got the upper hand; for it wasn't long before we, like the others, stood down by the duck pond, looking on.

We had come at just the right moment. On the south side of the pond stood Sven and Magnus in their bare feet, their trousers rolled above their knees, and their spades raised to cut through the bank of the pond. Papa gave the order: "One, two, three—go!"—with that the ditching began. The spades flashed as the men heaved the earth to one side, and water from the pond came rushing out into a narrow trench.

It gushed out merrily, bubbling and purling. We thought the water looked jubilant over its release. If it had only known that this was the end of the old duck pond, we said, perhaps it would not have run off with such glee.

It flowed rapidly over the ground to the south of the pond, where the turf had been removed, filling every hollow, and making a detour around each stone in its path, forcing its way farther and farther from the pond, pausing at times as if exhausted, until reinforcements coming from the pond sent it onward again, until it reached the gravel embankment, where it suddenly stopped. As it could advance no farther, it spread below the wall.

Sven of Paris and Magnus of Vienna dug and dug, and the water came pouring from the pond faster and faster, until the water itself did the work without their having to dig further. Just as through a dish with a hole in one side, the water flowed through the southern bank, forming many small rivulets that found their way to the wall, there to spread themselves out.

But after a while the water flowed more slowly; it collected in small pools and stood in puddles. To us children it looked as though the water was no longer so eager to escape from its old home. Then Sven of Paris and Magnus of Vienna dug a hole in the eastern bank. After that the water flowed faster. We had never imagined there was so much water in the old pond! It spread both to south and east, covering an area three times as large as that of the old duck pond.

Oh, but we children were stupid! There we stood, grieving and angry because our old pond would be no more. But at last we saw that instead of the pond being drained, it had become many times larger than it was before. If the pond was to be as big as that, we would have a great place to skate on. We actually turned giddy at the thought of it.

We saw and marvelled, but we could not express our delight until we were quite sure the pond was not being drained. Imagine our joy when we heard Papa say that he had decided it was better to widen the pond than to do away with it entirely! The water would be clearer and better when the pond had been enlarged. It could be used for washing clothes, and, in case of fire, we would have a pond large enough to fetch water from.

And all the grown-ups congratulated Papa on this great improvement. Though neither Papa nor the others mentioned the improved skating pond, we children felt that he had done this for us so that we would have more room to whirl about.

In the late summer, when the Hammargrens, the

Afzeliuses, Fru Hedberg, Uncle Kristofer, and Aunt
Julia came to Mårbacka, they were astonished to see
the new Mårbacka lake in place of the old duck pond.
And every morning Papa took Uncle Hammargren
and Uncle Oriel, Uncle Schenson and Uncle Kristofer
down to the pond to show them what he had done.
Here he had cut a hole through the wall for a drain
and put up a sluice gate so that too much water would
not escape. Then he took them up to the place where
he had dug a canal to convey the water from the
woods.

They thought it had all been admirably planned
and executed; but what they admired most was the
great culvert Papa had laid under the road for the
water to flow through into the lake. I don't think
Papa ever received so much praise for anything he
had done as for this ditching.

One evening when Uncle Schenson and Fru Hedberg returned from a walk in the twilight, they told
of a strange light they had seen hovering over the
pond. It was not moonlight, for the moon had not
yet risen; nor was it a reflection of the sunset, for that
evening the sun had been under a cloud. Supper was
on the table, but Mamma and all the guests—and
Papa, too, of course—rushed out to the pond to see
the strange shimmer.

Coming back, some said it was probably a tin of
anchovies that lay shining at the bottom of the pond;

others thought it must be phosphorescent wood which had been thrown into the water; but Fru Hedberg would not accept these conjectures. She said that which she had seen was a bluish phosphorescence rising from the water, and that there was something mystical and supernatural about it.

We children were down by the pond also, but we saw nothing remarkable, and we were inclined to believe it was something Fru Hedberg had imagined. But the mysterious light afforded the grown-ups much pleasure. Every evening they marched down to the pond in solemn procession to see the phosphorescent light rise from the water. And it created no end of controversy. Finally Uncle Oriel proposed that we call the new Mårbacka lake "Phosphoresque," to which they all agreed.

But the marvellous light that appeared every night on Mårbacka Lake became the talk of the whole countryside, and when the seventeenth of August came round again and Sexton Melanoz was to write his customary lyric in honour of Papa's anniversary, the pond figured largely in the birthday verses.

It was a long poem and was sung to the tune of "I Remember Those Blessed Days," by Fru Lenngren. The brothers Schullström and Herr Gustaf Asker and Fru Jacobson, a sister of the brothers Schullström, sang the verses lustily and well. All I can remember of the poem are the lines about the pond:

And this love of beauty
That made of a fen a lake,
Which to future generations
Will be known as Phosphoresque.

II

I do not recall that anything out of the ordinary happened to the pond that year. But the following spring Nurse Maja came up to the nursery one morning and told us that Mårbacka Lake had disappeared and that now the old duck pond was back again. That was all she would say. When we got dressed we could go and see for ourselves.

Naturally we had prided ourselves on having a lake at Mårbacka, like the one at Gårdsjö and at Herrestad. So we hurriedly put on our clothes and ran out. Then we saw with our own eyes that Nurse Maja had told the truth.

We were having our worst spring rains just then. The previous day the ice had broken up in Mårbacka Lake, and a magnificent sight it was. When the lake had cast off its coverlet of ice, the water rose to the edge of its banks, and quantities of water came rushing down.

But in the night it had rained so hard and the pond had become so full of water that it washed away the whole wall that Sven and Magnus had put up the previous summer. We were aghast when we saw the havoc the storm had wrought. It had torn away large stones and hurled them far out in the meadow, and had thrown the gravel even farther away. The willow slips that Papa had planted on top of the embankment were now on their way down to Lake Fryken.

Here was the abomination of desolation! The entire area where the water had risen so proudly the day before now lay waste. There was nothing left of the beautiful lake but soft clay with here and there a puddle of water. The old duck pond, however, had not been disturbed.

There it lay, nestling securely in its bed—a small round body of water—no larger, no smaller than it had been before. We thought, as we looked at it, that it smiled with mischievous glee, as if proclaiming it had come into its own again.

But Papa couldn't let the pond remain as it was of old. He had received more praise for this work of improvement than for any of his other undertakings. Hadn't the sexton written a poem about it? Hadn't all the relatives been keenly interested? And hadn't Fru Hedberg seen that marvellous blue shimmer hovering over the waters of the pond? The reputation of the whole property was at stake.

Although they were busy with the spring work, Papa could not rest until the wall had been rebuilt. The men had to haul stone and gravel down to the

pond and do masonry work instead of harrowing
and sowing. Lars of London and Magnus of Vienna
shook their heads in dismay at these orders. Per,
being a Finn, understood the mysteries of water. He
said right out that all this labour was useless. Something that lived in the old duck pond wanted it left
the way it had been from time immemorial.

However, the wall was put up and covered not only
with gravel like the former one but also with sod.
And two rows of willow slips were planted on the
wall, which were to send their roots down between the
stones, to help hold them together. It was a good job,
and after a few heavy showers, the lake was again
filled with water. When in August the guests arrived,
Mårbacka Lake lay there, glimmering and shining
just as it had the previous summer. The only differ-
ence was that Fru Hedberg's blue phosphorescence
was not to be seen on the surface of the water; it
must have been washed away by the devastating
storms of the spring.

The following year Papa took special precautions
during the breaking up of the ice. Every day he
examined the wall, inch by inch, for cracks through
which the water could seep. If he found so much as a
drop of water leaking out, he had his workmen
strengthen the wall with more stones and mortar and
gravel. If it rained in the night, Papa arose and went

down to the pond to be on hand in case anything should happen.

The whole house was always in a state of unrest on account of that pond! No one had any peace of mind until the spring rains were over. Cracks in the wall occurred regularly every spring and the wall had to be mended or braced continually, but it was not washed away until the year that Papa came home with inflammation of the lungs, from sleeping between damp sheets.

Mamma had no time to think of the pond or to have the cracks in the wall stopped. The breaking of the ice came early that spring, and by Easter everything went wrong. The stableman came in on Easter Eve to tell us that the water had begun to force its way under the wall. Mamma said it was too bad, but he must try to find someone to help him. But that was impossible. It was Easter Sunday, and the workmen in all the cottages had brought home brandy, and they wouldn't bother about the lake. Anyhow, the lake was man-made, they said, and had been on the place only a couple of years.

And so on Easter Sunday the water was allowed to work all the damage it could, and by Monday morning the entire wall had collapsed and lay scattered over the meadows, while the whole lake bottom was exposed—except the old duck pond. That lay securely within its banks, round as ever, and twinkled and gleamed as if happy at being again master of all it surveyed.

Papa, who was well enough now to sit up, was informed that the wall had broken down a second time. He became so disheartened that we feared he would have a relapse. But the first thing he did when he was able to take hold of things himself was to raise the wall for the third time.

He was not very happy at having to rebuild the wall once more. There was all the spring work to be done, and the farm labourers were tired of the everlasting bother with the pond, which was of no earthly use to anyone. But there was nothing to do but rebuild, since Papa insisted that the honour of his estate demanded that Mårbacka Lake should be restored. Considering all the praise showered upon him, he couldn't revert to the old duck pond.

While the workmen were rebuilding the wall, Uncle Wachenfeldt came driving down to Mårbacka in his little carriole. He had heard that Papa was ill and had come to see how it was with him. When he saw the men at work on the new wall, he drew rein and shook his head. Then, as he drove toward the house, he said to Papa: "If you put up your wall in that way, Erik Gustaf, you will have to rebuild it every year."

"You don't say so, Wachenfeldt! Now you're very clever. I wish you would tell me of a better way."

"Don't fill it in with loose gravel if you want the wall to hold, but put the gravel into sacks as they do in war time when building a trench."

Papa followed his advice, and from that time to this the wall has stood; for which we are all thankful. Every spring it had been a source of anxiety to us, as each day we expected to hear that the wall had collapsed again.

III

Shortly after Papa had built a wall that would hold, he went to Strömstad. While down by the sea, he must have thought of his lake and have seen what it lacked by comparing it with Kattegat. At all events, he had no sooner returned than he undertook further improvements.

He again planted a row of willows on either side of the wall and laid a gravelled walk between them so the folks would have a shore promenade like the one at Laholmen, in Strömstad. And he said that when the willows were grown he would build a pavilion at the southeast corner of the wall, from which the view was the loveliest. And in his old age he would sit in the pavilion in August when the harvest moon was full and see the trees which he had planted mirrored in the waters of the lake.

The willows grew and flourished, but everything

else that Papa tried to do to beautify the pond failed. Poor Papa! I felt so sorry for him.

In the summer, when Daniel and Johan were at home, Daniel always helped Aunt Lovisa with the flowers. He loved to work in the garden, hoeing and weeding like a regular gardener. Aunt Lovisa was glad of the help he gave her. But Johan, on the contrary, had a bent for mechanics.

When Papa got back from Strömstad, Johan suggested that he let him build a craft of some sort to sail the pond. As Papa had been out sailing every day at Strömstad, he thought that if Mårbacka Lake only had boats it wouldn't be so far behind Kattegat; so he promised at once to let the boy try.

Johan made a small raft about eight feet square and nailed an empty ale keg under each corner so that it could carry a heavy cargo without sinking. Then he made an engine out of an old spinning wheel and an oven rake—the rake to go underneath the boat and the wheel above. Johan was to stand behind the wheel and steer. The moment he turned the wheel, the propeller under the water would begin to work and the boat would skim across the lake from shore to shore.

We were elated over Johan's invention. Now, we thought, he would be able to sail the pond, and we wondered if he might not be another John Ericsson. But we were wrong. When he turned the spinning wheel the boat did not move. So that hope was dashed.

But there was much else that moved on the waters at Strömstad besides boats and ships. There were also wild ducks and eider ducks. Papa decided he would have waterfowl, too. So he wrote to some place in West Gothnia for geese. And one fine day there came to Herrestad Pier seven goslings, which the stableman was ordered to fetch.

Everyone said they were fine geese. They were by no means small; on the contrary, they were nearly full grown. Aunt Lovisa said it was a pleasure to have geese on the place as in her parents' time, and the housekeeper told us about the gander that flew away with the wild geese one spring, when Fru Raklitz ruled at Mårbacka, and came back in the autumn with a mate and nine half-grown goslings. We were disappointed because the geese were not white, but the grown-ups said they were just as good as the white geese.

The geese were penned up in the cow barn for a week so that they would become accustomed to the place and not stray when we let them out. On the eighth day they were allowed to move about in the barnyard. And, indeed, they were tame and well behaved! They did not chase you or nip at your skirts, as geese generally do, but directly they were let out they went over to the nearest meadow and began cropping grass, as if they were cows or sheep.

We children were eager to see the geese swim, but as the lake was at some distance from the cow barn Papa thought they had better stay in the barnyard. In the morning, when they had become more accustomed to their surroundings, we might let them go swimming in Mårbacka Lake.

There is a small pond near the barn where the cows drink after grazing in the meadow, but we were so impatient to see the West Gothnia geese swim that we drove them to the little pond. We had always thought that geese would be so glad of the least little pool of water that they would dive in at once. But these geese simply would not go down to the byre pond. Then we said it must be because they were used to better things, that they would not go down into a dirty pond. It would be different in the morning when they could swim in nice clear water.

Next day we drove the geese to the big pond; but apparently the fine West Gothnia geese did not see how much better this was than the byre pond. They walked all around the banks of Mårbacka Lake, honking and nibbling grass, and did not even look at the water, much less stick their bills into it.

Uncle Schenson said that the West Gothnia geese had grown up on a farm where there was no open body of water, and therefore they had not learned to swim when they were goslings. They did not know they were waterfowl.

We tried to accustom them to the lake by throwing bread crumbs on the water, to make them swim out after the bread; but they only strove to get back on land. The geese were more afraid of water than were our turkeys.

I remember how, once, all the boys and girls at Mårbacka formed a half-circle round the geese and drove them down to the lake. When the geese reached the edge of the water and saw that there was no way of escape, they spread their small wings and flew in terror to the opposite shore—glad they had managed to save themselves from drowning.

So one could truthfully say that Papa had no luck with his attempts to beautify the place, and we really pitied him. But Papa was not one to give up so easily. He must have thought that, since he could not have boats and water birds floating on the surface of the lake, he would have better luck with things that live and move in the water.

So he made arrangements with some small boys who lived near Gårdsjö Lake to catch a lot of small fish for him. And every Sunday, when the boys were free from school, they came to Mårbacka carrying big bucketfuls of roach and perch which Papa emptied into the lake. Every day for a whole week Papa and we children stood out on the bank and cast bread crumbs to the fishes.

But it seemed strange that, although he had poured such great quantities of small fish into the pond every Sunday, we never saw them afterwards. They never appeared at the surface of the water and never bobbed up to catch gnats, as fishes usually do at dusk. They all disappeared at once; and yet they couldn't have died or they would have floated upon the surface.

"They must have escaped through the drain," said Papa. And he put up a grating at the mouth of the drain which would let the water flow through but not the fishes.

When the boys came again on Sunday, bringing their perch and roach, the grating had been put up. Now he knew the fish could not escape. But his joy was of short duration; for the following morning the pond was literally covered with tiny dead fish. It was a ghastly sight as they floated there, pale and bloated, their bellies exposed to the air. To think that just the previous evening they had been swimming about on their tiny fins, and now they were dead! It was enough to make the angels weep!

We children said among ourselves that Papa would have to give up his attempts, for now it was plain that no fish could live in our lake. But a few days later we heard Papa ask Sven of Paris if he, who had run about the woods all his life, did not know of some pool where carp were to be found.

Sven of Paris scratched his head and pondered a moment; then he said that when he was a small boy he and his father had once fished for carp in a pool far up among the Gårdsjö hills. "We did not catch them with hooks," he said, "but set out a trough in which we had spread some dough, and soon after we had lowered the trough into the water it was full of fish. They were fat carp and glittered like gold, but they weren't much good for eating. When we brought them home, Mother didn't want to prepare them. She said they tasted like clay, and she was right about it."

But the very next Sunday Papa sent Sven of Paris up to the pools in the Gårdsjö hills to catch carp for him. Sven took with him a baking trough, a clump of dough, and a brass kettle to put the fish in. All this was done with the utmost secrecy. I don't think even Mamma or Aunt Lovisa knew on what sort of errand Sven had gone. Only we children knew.

We waited all day Sunday, but Sven did not appear. Perhaps he could not find the carp pool, we said; and had given up the search and gone home. On Monday Sven of Paris came, as usual, at five in the morning to help the milkmaid curry the cows and drive them out to pasture. But not a word did he say about carp.

When Papa had finished his breakfast he went down to the barnyard, where he met Sven, trundling a wheelbarrow. "Well, Sven," he said, "did you find the carp pool?"

"Sure I found it," said Sven of Paris. "But I had to tramp about in the woods all day Sunday."

"Did you catch any carp?"

"None worth talking about. Only small fry came to the bake trough to eat dough. The big fish must have been asleep at the bottom of the pool."

"So you thought it would not pay to bring the small fry home?"

"No. Sure they were nothing to carry home," said Sven of Paris.

"But what became of the brass kettle and the dough trough?"

"I put them in the servants' hall when I came back this morning."

Papa must have felt as though he were being pursued by ill luck, but he took it with his usual calm. He gave Sven a riksdaler for his trouble and bade us children go over to the servants' hall for the brass kettle and dough trough and take them into the kitchen.

We found the brass kettle full of water, in which were a lot of tiny fishes, the smallest we had ever seen. We ran out to Papa as fast as we could and showed him the fish. He was delighted. They were

genuine carp. Why Sven of Paris had not told him
that he had the carp, no one knew. But, as Papa
would say, Sven had his own way of doing things.

We dropped the fish into the lake. No one knew
but Papa and us children that they were there. And
Papa said we were not to tell anyone. "We must
first see how the fish thrive," he told us.

As the grating was up before the outlet, there was
no way for the young carp to escape; but we feared
that they might meet the same fate as the perch
and roach from Gårdsjö Lake. No carp, however,
were seen to drift lifeless on the pond next morning.
Twice a week Papa took us up to the storeroom and
filled our aprons with grains of rye, which we cast on
the water as food for the carp. We never saw any of
them, and we were almost certain they had slipped
away, but anyhow we did as Papa bade us.

Sometimes, when we sat down to dinner, Papa
complained because there was only meat on the
table day after day. "You must remember that
Schenson comes from Karlstad," he would say to
Aunt Lovisa. "And one who lives but a stone's throw
from the Klar River is accustomed to having fish for
his dinner."

Papa only said that because he himself preferred
fish to meat; but the remark embarrassed Uncle
Schenson; he was afraid Aunt Lovisa might think he
was dissatisfied with the food served at Mårbacka,

and hastened to turn the matter aside with a jest.

"We'll have to do without fish until we can take it out of Mårbacka Lake," he said.

That silenced Papa; for he did not want Aunt Lovisa or Uncle Schenson to know about the carp.

We continued to cast rye on the water, until it began to freeze over. After it had frozen solid, Papa went out on the ice every day to see that there was an air hole in the ice, so that the carp could breathe.

When the winter was over and summer had come, we went again with Papa to the storeroom to have our aprons filled with rye to cast upon the waters of the lake. And we kept this up for several years without having seen so much as the tail of a fish. It was sinful, we thought, to throw away so much good rye uselessly, but we did it, all the same.

IV

To think that this is Papa's birthday—oh, what in the world shall we do! Jansson went down to the landing this morning to fetch the salmon that had been ordered from Karlstad, and he has just come back to tell us that there was no fish on the boat.

The housekeeper and Aunt Lovisa and Mamma, too, are almost frantic. They don't know what to do, and they will have to tell Papa, who is out on the porch with Uncle Schenson, how badly things have turned out.

"Here we're expecting a hundred guests to sup-per," says Aunt Lovisa, "and we have no salmon."

"Don't you think it would be advisable to send word to the Gårdsjö folk to bring a few pike along when they come?" Mamma suggests.

"I suppose that is the best we can do under the circumstances," Aunt Lovisa says. "But it's provok-ing, all the same, not to have anything better than a few half-starved pike to set before our guests."

"So it is," says Uncle Schenson. "This would be a fitting occasion to serve some fish from Mårbacka Lake."

When Papa hears that, he can't hold in any longer. Now, he thinks, is the proper time to reveal the secret.

"Don't be uneasy, Lovisa. There will be plenty of fish for supper, and we'll have it here in less than an hour."

With that he puts on his hat and goes out to find Daniel and Johan and bid them take a message to Pastor Lindegren, at Halla. We know that Pastor Lindegren loves to fish, and several times he has taken the boys with him on long fishing trips; but we don't see how he can help us out. He can't have put out any lines today, surely; so it isn't likely that he will have any fish before tomorrow morning, and by that time the birthday party will be over.

But in a moment we see Pastor Lindegren and the

boys coming down the road. The boys are lugging a
heavy net, and the pastor himself is carrying a long
fishing rod over his shoulder. They are coming to the
house, but stop first at the pond.

Then everyone rushes down to the pond—the home
folk, the Hammargrens, the Afzeliuses, Fru Hedberg,
and all the cousins who have come to Mårbacka to
celebrate Papa's birthday. Pastor Lindegren stands
out on the small washing bridge at the northeast end
and lowers his fishing pole into the water. He moves
it back and forth very carefully, but when he draws
it up there is no fish on the hook.

"Just as we expected," the guests remark. What
kind of fish did they expect to find in the pond?
"Only frogs can live there," says Uncle Schenson.

But Pastor Lindegren does not give up. He unties
the net, while Daniel and Johan take off their heavy
shoes and stockings and wade in, dragging the net
along the banks of the pond to the opposite shore.
Then, lowering the net, they drag it a short distance
over the bed of the pond.

With that, there is life in the water. It bubbles as if
it were boiling. A furious splashing is heard; then a
swift ripple, and suddenly a big shining, yellow fish
bobs up to the surface.

Pastor Lindegren is so excited he can hardly con-
tain himself. He shouts an order to the boys to haul
up the seine, and they quickly raise it to the surface.

The net is full of glittering golden fish. It is as if they fished up nuggets of gold.

"What say you now, Schenson?" asks Papa. "Don't you think these 'frogs' will make good eating?"

Pastor Lindegren stands there, looking radiant and proud, but the one who looks still more radiant is my father. Now he feels amply repaid for all the humiliations he has suffered and for all the cutting remarks he has endured. He receives again praise and congratulations as at the time when the pond was newly dredged and was called Lake Phosphoresque.

Aunt Nana Hammargren and Aunt Georgina Afzelius stand a little apart from the others, talking in undertones, while the carp are being taken out of the net. They do not see that I am standing close beside them, or perhaps they think that a little girl like me will not understand anything; for that is what the grown-ups usually think.

"I don't like this thing, Georgina," says Aunt Nana. "In former years when we came to Mårbacka, Gustaf was eager to show us the improvements he had made. He had extended his property by the purchase of adjacent land, or put up new buildings, or laid out gardens, or planted oak trees and Lombardy poplars. There was always something useful or beautiful for us to see, but all he thinks of now is that dreadful pond."

"Let me tell you, Nana, that Louise is worried about Gustaf. She says he is far from well, that he has been ailing ever since he had that severe lung trouble, three years ago."

"He has gone grey uncommonly fast," observes Aunt Nana thoughtfully.

"And he has fallen away also."

"But what does his illness have to do with the pond?"

"Well, you see, Louise believes that Gustaf is no longer able to undertake any regular work, but that he must have something to potter with, to make it appear that he is accomplishing something."

"My poor brother!" Aunt Nana says with a heavy sigh.

It is a pity that I should have heard this on Papa's birthday when we usually have such a jolly time! My heart aches for him—it hurts me so dreadfully! I shall feel this as long as I live.

XX
AGRIPPA PRÄSTBERG

THE young folks are dancing in the dining room. But even if someone were to ask me I could not dance after what I overheard this morning. I am standing on the porch instead, where the old gentlemen are seated around a large table with their steaming toddy glasses before them, and I am listening to their anecdotes.

I don't know how they happened upon the subject of that old vagabond, Agrippa Prästberg—he who comes here every spring to mend the kitchen clock. I would rather hear about the great heroes who lived when the old gentlemen were young. But now that Prästberg is on the carpet, they are not likely to let him go for some time to come.

It seems strange that all the men like to talk of Agrippa Prästberg! I shudder every time I see him. He has a big hook nose with no less than three humps on it. His bushy beard stands out like the bristles on a porcupine, and his eyes are yellow as bile. He never has a kind or a civil word for anyone, but growls and curses wherever he goes. He makes me think of a savage old wolf.

Prästberg boasts that he has served as a drummer with the Värmland Cavalry, and therefore Papa regards him as an old comrade-at-arms and is always kind to him. Papa knows as well as we that Prästberg does not understand the first thing about repairing clocks, but all the same he allows him to stop here for days at a time and tinker with the kitchen clock. But Aunt Lovisa never lets him touch the clock in her room, and as for the new clock in the dining room, Mamma has given strict orders not to allow him so much as to look at it. The kitchen clock he has already ruined past repair.

So when Prästberg comes in the spring and asks for work, Papa lets him amuse himself with the kitchen clock. He takes it apart, greases it with neat's-foot oil, files and hammers at the wheels and puts it together again. This work he manages to drag out three days at the least. Meantime he litters up the kitchen with his tools and grease jars so that it is positively unbearable for the housekeeper and the maids. When at last he has finished and put the clock back on the shelf, the pendulum swings until Präst-berg has reached the highway, when it stops; and no one touches the clock again until he comes back the following year to "regulate" it.

Papa is not the only one, however, who likes Agrippa Prästberg. All the gentlemen of East Ämtervik are eager to regale Uncle Oriel and Uncle Hammargren and other guests who have not heard of him before with stories of his doings. But they recount only the old Prästberg yarns which I have already heard a thousand times.

When he lived in a small cottage down by the East Ämtervik church he treated his wife so brutally that the neighbours feared he would kill her. But the Christmas holidays were for her the most dreadful of all; for then there were brandy flasks in every corner of the house. The brothers Schullström, whose shop was next door to Prästberg's cottage, took pity on the poor woman and determined to see that for once she had a peaceful Christmas. So on Christmas Eve they sent for Prästberg and handed him a thick envelope bearing a large seal, to which a feather was attached. They told him the letter had been left by a special courier and that he, as a servant of the realm, was to deliver it into the hands of Captain Belfrage, at Karlstad. Prästberg promptly set off on his mission, travelling day and night, and in stormy weather to boot. He did not return until the third day after Christmas.

In the meantime he had discovered that the "letter" contained only straw and shavings. He was provoked at himself for being so easily hoaxed by the brothers Schullström, and decided to shake the dust of East Ämtervik from his feet at once. He moved to Sunne, where he hung around the shops and ran errands for the shopkeepers whenever it suited him.

The East Ämtervik gentlemen then tell of the curious abode Prästberg had built for himself. He had gathered up some half-rotten logs and board ends that lay about the farmyards, and of these he had made a raft which he floated on the lake. On the raft he built a small house, where he spent his summers. The houseboat had a floor, a roof, windows, and a door. And it was furnished with a stove, a bed, a planing bench, and a turner's lathe. Out on the raft there was plenty of room for Prästberg to sit and fish his dinner out of the Fryken. He had a punt tied to the raft and could go ashore whenever he wished. Moreover, he could move his house; so when he tired of the eastern side he could tow it over to the western.

Once when we went to Karlstad by boat, I saw Prästberg's house lying in a snug little inlet. I said to myself: "One who lives like that, in a house on the water, is not to be pitied but rather to be envied." It looked so cozy that I should have liked to have just such a houseboat to live in myself.

Sexton Melanoz had found a good name for the

boat—he called it *Moses*. When the others hear that, they go into roars of laughter and shake their heads at the sexton. But how could a sexton and a teacher of the young be so impious! What must the clergymen who are present think!

The sexton apparently is not at all abashed. "Let me tell you, gentlemen, that Prästberg's *Moses* as it lay mirroring itself in the waters of the lake was the snuggest little thing I've ever seen. Even an Egyptian princess might well have taken a fancy to *Moses*. That boat is regarded as one of the famous sights of this region. Last summer a reporter from the *Värmland News* came here to make a sketch of the boat, and he wrote a long story about it for the paper."

"*Skål*, Melanoz!" says Papa. "Don't let those Stockholmers make mincemeat of you. Defend yourself! For you can do it."

Papa raises his glass and drinks a health to him. He likes the sexton and has always maintained that if Melanoz had had as many advantages in his youth as the young folks have nowadays, he would have invented a flying machine that could travel to the moon.

"But since we are talking of *Moses*," the sexton continues, "with your permission I'll tell you a story —something that happened about seven or eight years ago."

Needless to say, the sexton is allowed to proceed.

As this is a Prästberg story I have not heard before, I listen with keen interest.

"I don't know how it came about," the sexton begins, "but old Agrippa must have grown a bit vain over all the compliments showered upon his *Moses*, and so he decided to give him a coat of red. He went around to the various shops in Sunne and borrowed red ochre, a pot to boil it in, and brushes; and then one day he began boiling reddle. As *Moses* lay in the vicinity of Sunne Deanery, directly below Sund Bridge, everyone who crossed the bridge could see what he was doing, which perhaps was his intention."

"Oh, it's that story!" says Papa—far from pleased. "Can't you give us something else, Melanoz?"

Despite Papa's protest, the sexton goes on with his story: "As I remarked a moment ago, an Egyptian princess might have conceived a fondness for *Moses*, and I must confess that I myself have a certain affection for him. But the most ardent friends and admirers of *Moses* are to be found among the children. As soon as they catch sight of the boat they gather on the shore and cast yearning glances in its direction; for, you see, they are never allowed on board. And now that *Moses* was being painted, a crowd of youngsters had gathered on Sund Bridge to watch."

"Get on with the story, Melanoz!" says Papa. "It will soon be time to light the Chinese lanterns."

"You see, Lieutenant," the sexton continues, "as luck would have it, while Prästberg was painting for dear life, word came from Merchant Rystedt of Lerbrobacken that he must come at once to peddle fish. Rystedt had got a big run of fish that morning, which he had to dispose of. It was a warm day, so the fish would spoil quickly lying in the shop. Important though it was that *Moses* should be painted, Prästberg did not dare to say no to Tradesman Rystedt; for he had the finest shop in town, and the one in which Prästberg usually found refuge in winter. So, laying down his paintbrush, he rowed ashore and went from house to house peddling fish."

"Oh!" Uncle Oriel breaks in. "But he chased the boys away first, didn't he?"

"That's just what he neglected to do," says the sexton. "Perhaps he thought the youngsters, knowing him of old, would be afraid to touch his property. But it stands to reason, since the boys had been deprived of their pleasure, they would become impatient. They had hoped to see *Moses* in a new coat of red before nightfall, and naturally felt disappointed. But after a little an imp of mischief suggested to them that they help Prästberg decorate his boat. There was no harm intended; it was simply because they liked *Moses* and wanted to see him dressed up. When the idea came to them, they wasted no time in vain speculation but promptly set off for the village to beg, borrow, or steal the necessary brushes. In some places they got them for the asking, and at others they helped themselves. Finding a boat to take them out to *Moses* was an easy matter."

At this point in the story, Johan and Daniel, Teodor Hammargren and Ernest Schenson came out to light the lanterns. A crowd of young girls and young men who have been dancing come out on the porch and stand listening to the sexton. Everyone, I believe, finds the story amusing—everyone but Papa, who wishes the sexton would stop. But he goes right on:

"The children set to work with a will, and the boat was soon painted. But when they had made it red as a rose from top to bottom on the outside they began to think that painting was great sport, and decided to continue. There was enough red ochre left to paint a two-story house, and of course they had brushes. Anyone who in adolescence has ever dabbled in paint knows how easily he can get into a painting frenzy and must daub everything in sight with colour."

"Now, Melanoz," says Papa, "I think you have made excuses enough for those boys. Let us get on with the story."

"Well, perhaps I did make excuses for the boys, but, believe me, it was necessary. The first thing they painted was the raft on which the house rested.

There was no harm in that, surely. Then they painted the chimney and the roof, which was innocent enough, and while they were in a painting mood they decided to do the interior of the houseboat also. They proceeded to paint the walls, the ceiling, and the floor. The boys didn't know that reddle was not suitable for interiors. It never gets thoroughly dry and rubs off if you touch it. But the worst of it was, the boys were having such heaps of fun that they wouldn't stop until they had painted the planing bench, the bed, the chairs, the table, all the tools and the household utensils. The Lieutenant thinks I'm soft where children are concerned; that no matter to what lengths they go, I always find excuses for them. But that isn't so. I said it was shameful of the boys to spoil Prästberg's boat, and I really felt sorry for the poor old man. Indeed, I should hate to have been in Prästberg's boots when he saw what the youngsters had done to his boat."

"What did he do?" asks Uncle Oriel, laughing. "*Fi donc!* To come home and find your mugs, glasses, and spoons, your bed and bedding covered with reddle was no joke. He must have given those young rascals a sound thrashing."

"No," says the sexton, "he didn't. Old Agrippa became so disheartened when he saw what they had done to his property that he just laid him down in the punt—the only thing that hadn't been reddled—and there he remained, motionless as stone. But there was someone whose wrath was aroused—I don't know whether I may tell what followed," he says with a side-glance at Papa, who answers him brusquely:

"Since you have told that much, you may as well tell it all."

"Well, then," observes the sexton, "I was about to say, the one whose wrath was aroused was Lieutenant Lagerlöf. When he heard of the outrage he decided to go at once to Sunne and give those youngsters a good whaling. Fru Lagerlöf tried to dissuade him from doing anything so rash. As it happened in Sunne, she said, where he had no authority, perhaps *he* would be punished instead of the boys. But the Lieutenant, who regarded Prästberg as an old companion-in-arms, felt that someone ought to take the poor fellow's part; so off he went."

It has grown quite dark outside, and I catch the gleam of the first lanterns as the boys run about to hang them. Then all at once the heavens become indigo blue and the tall Lombardy poplars beyond the circular sward look quite black. The night is calm and peaceful and my heart grows light. I do not care what became of Prästberg, but all the same I think it was fine of Papa to go to his defense.

"Aye, he went to Sunne," the sexton continues with a cryptic smile. "But as he was driving by the rectory, the dean and his daughter Eva, who had just returned from their morning walk, were standing outside. The Lieutenant, who has always been very fond of Professor Fryxell, jumped down from his carriole and went over to greet them.

"They asked him to come in and chat awhile. Professor Fryxell always had many things of interest to relate, and having known the Lieutenant and liked him since the latter was a small boy, he was glad to see him. They had many things in common, and after they had been talking a full hour, the Lieutenant suddenly remembered why he had come to Sunne. He sprang up saying, 'I must go now.'"

I feel so sorry for Papa! Listening to all this talk about himself is painful to him. He turns and twists uneasily in his chair, as if he could stand no more.

"But Mamselle Eva Fryxell doubtless had noted that her father was enjoying the company of Lieutenant Lagerlöf," the sexton continues, "and begged him not to be in such haste to leave. Couldn't he stay to dinner? When the Lieutenant declined, on account of urgent business, she wanted to know the nature of the business. At last the Lieutenant had to tell her. And of course the Professor heard it, too."

"Ha!" cries Uncle Hammargren, "he was just the one to settle with those boys!"

"Yes, I think it can be truly said that he was," the sexton agrees, "for, as I have already remarked, the Professor liked the Lieutenant. As soon as he

heard the story about Prästberg, he took the Lieutenant by the hand and led him into his study. For
my humble part, whenever I enter that room I feel
as if I were stepping into a sanctuary—away from
all that is petty and mean; and doubtless Lieutenant
Lagerlöf felt as I do. The Professor now opened a
drawer of his writing desk and showed the Lieutenant
a huge collection of letters and press cuttings.

"'In this drawer,' he said, 'I keep all that was
written about me at the time I gave out Volumes 22
to 29 of my historical work—those dealing with
Charles XII. They were no light strokes that were
applied to me then, I can tell you. Indeed they went
at me harder than the children went at Prästberg's
boat. I was painted in the blackest colours and held
up to scorn, and they were applied to me personally,
and not merely to my books. My dear Erik Gustaf,
good friends we have been always, but you didn't
fare forth with rising gorge to thrash my attackers.'

"The Professor had spoken kindly but with a
waggish glint in his eyes. Suddenly he laughed.
'No, no, Erik Gustaf! That is not the way to go
about it. I know that we Swedes, you in particular
and I to a certain extent, are fond of adventurers—
madcaps like Agrippa Prästberg and Charles XII;
and that is why you came here to punish those Sunne
youngsters who played Prästberg a mean trick. But,
Erik Gustaf, do you think it worth while for Lieu-

tenant Lagerlöf to constitute himself that fellow's champion? Here in Sunne we regard him as a veritable plague to the countryside. Yet you, a respected and capable——'"

Papa can stand no more. "Have a care, Melanoz!" he warns him and raps on the table with his knuckles.

"Yes, yes, Lieutenant, I'll soon be through. I merely want to tell how it ended."

It is well that Papa has rapped on the table, for otherwise I fear the sexton would talk all night about Professor Fryxell, who had made it possible for him —the son of humble peasants—to rise to the status of sexton and schoolmaster.

"It was a foregone conclusion that the Lieutenant would have to give in," the sexton continues. "He promised to stay for dinner, and to go straight home afterward and not throw himself into any foolhardy adventure on Prästberg's account. I must say that to wrestle with a fighter like Professor Fryxell is not easy. One feels so small and insignificant in his presence, though one may think oneself a pretty clever fellow when with others. So I can understand why the Lieutenant gave in, and I also understand that he must have felt displeased with himself for having failed his companion-in-arms. And the Professor I daresay understood——"

Again Papa raps on the table.

"Yes, yes, Lieutenant. I have only a few words

more to add. After dinner the Professor took the Lieutenant with him out to the garden. They walked down the broad steps between the terraces leading to Lake Fryken. When they came to the lowest terrace, which extends over the water, what should they see right before them but *Moses* and the little punt, in which Prästberg lay grieving as he had grieved since the day the boys played havoc with his property.

"'There you see, Uncle, it is just as I told you,' the Lieutenant hastened to point out. 'He can no longer occupy his house.'

"'Yes, I see,' said the Professor. He walked to the far end of the parapet and looked down upon *Moses*. 'What do you think of this reddle, my dear Erik Gustaf?' he asked. For Professor Fryxell's sharp eyes saw at a glance that *Moses* was not red, but a dirty gray. The water around the boat, however, was red.

"The Professor then leaned over the parapet and shouted: 'I say, Prästberg, did you blend any rye meal with the red ochre when you boiled it?'

"'Good Lord!' he cried. 'I clean forgot to mix in the rye!'

"Prästberg knew of course that rye should be mixed with red ochre or it would rub off as easily as chalk. But he had been in such haste to paint *Moses* that he had not thought of the rye.

"'It was a lucky thing for you, Prästberg,' said the Professor. 'For now you will soon be able to move back to your houseboat.'

"The Professor then turned to the Lieutenant and said: 'Let us go in now and consult with these benevolent daughters of mine, Louise and Matilda. They know all the children in the parish and can soon find out which ones were responsible for this mischief. These youngsters will then have the task of scouring *Moses* clean, both inside and outside. For some punishment must be meted out to them, and this, I believe, will be a more effective lesson to them than any corporal punishment. By this means, Prästberg will have his houseboat again, and you, my dear Erik Gustaf, can go back to your home conscious of a duty well performed.'"

Papa raps on the table for the third time.

"I understand," says the sexton, "that I mustn't tell how the Lieutenant thanked the Professor. But we'll let that pass."

Then the sexton rises and, holding up his glass of toddy, says:

"Herr Lieutenant Lagerlöf, I'm sure we are all glad that you went to Sunne that time to help your old comrade-at-arms, and I propose that we give three cheers for Lieutenant Lagerlöf."

So they shout, "Hurrah, hurrah, hurrah!" When the cheering is over we notice the illumination. All the magic lanterns have been hung. The flowers in Aunt Lovisa's beds have become transparent as if made of spun glass. Back in the bushes the foliage shimmers in all the colours of the rainbow. The night air is still and balmy, and there is something delicately fragrant that fills the heart with joy.

On the gravelled path at the foot of the steps stand the brothers Schullström and Jan Asker singing:

Who does not remember our brother!

XXI
AT THE PIER

We are driving down to Herrestad Pier with a wagonload of luggage. Uncle Schenson, with Ernst, Klaës, and Alma, is leaving for Karlstad, and Uncle Oriel Afzelius and Aunt Georgina, with their children, Elin and Allan, are going back to Stockholm.

Just as they are ready to start, Papa says there is room in one of the carriages for two of us children, if we would like to come along; so that is how Gerda and I happen to go. We do not have a very comfortable seat on the way down, but we know we can sit in the back seat going home, which is really why we go.

Papa is always very particular to have his guests allow themselves plenty of time when they are going by boat. Therefore the farewell breakfast was served promptly at nine. At ten o'clock we are on our way, and by eleven we are down at the pier.

We shall have to wait there at least an hour, for the *Anders Fryxell* is not due at Herrestad until twelve. Uncle Schenson and Uncle Oriel are none too pleased at the early start, but Papa says that something might happen on the way to delay them—the horses might go lame or a wheel ring might get loose; therefore, he thinks it best to be a little ahead of time.

We all run out to the far end of the pier to watch for the steamer; and, as is to be expected, she is not in sight. Aunt Georgina goes to a wooded hill near by and sits down on a ledge of rock. Uncle Oriel flings himself on the moss at her feet and, pulling his hat over his face, says: "Don't forget to wake me when the boat comes." Uncle Schenson sits down on the rock beside Aunt Georgina to chat.

"I say, Cousin Schenson, you may as well lie down beside Oriel and take a little nap, too. I'll keep watch and will call you when the boat arrives."

We children all go for a stroll in Herrestad Park. We see Engineer Noreen's once beautiful pavilion, which now, alas, has fallen into decay. (The Noreens, by the way, have left Herrestad and are now living on a small estate near the church.) We also visit the Grotto of the Bear and show our cousins the wonderful blackberry vines which are not to be found anywhere else in the parish.

We walk slowly, knowing we have a whole hour to

wait, and finally sit down in the shade of the pine tree that hangs over the edge of the bear pit. We talk of what would happen if the bear were to clamber up.

As we sit there, a man comes running toward us, shouting: "The steamer has left Sunne and is lying-to at Rottneros; she should be here in half an hour."

We spring to our feet and rush down to the pier. We see smoke in the distance and a dark object that moves toward the shore to the northeast. Now everyone is glad that Papa has been in such haste to start them off, for otherwise they might have missed the boat.

Uncle Oriel, Aunt Georgina, and Uncle Schenson are looking to see whether they have brought all their boxes, bags, and baskets with them, and Aunt Georgina gives directions as to what pieces each is to carry on board. Everyone knows, of course, that the boat won't be here for another half-hour.

But one can't always be sure about a steamer. Sometimes, when violent storms are raging, she can't lay-to at Herrestad Pier at all, or when she has a couple of big barges in tow, she cannot get down to Fryksta Landing. We all feel relieved now that the boat has reached Rottneros.

"I'm glad to know that we shall soon be on our way," says Uncle Schenson. "Perhaps it was a bit rash of me to stay until the last moment, but it is always so hard to tear oneself away from dear old Mårbacka!"

"Does your school open tomorrow, Cousin?" Aunt Georgina asks.

"Yes; tomorrow at ten," says Uncle Schenson. "I daresay you think me an incurable sentimentalist, Georgina?"

"I think that of all men," Aunt Georgina retorts. "Oriel does precisely the same thing. He has to take up his official duties at Stockholm the day after tomorrow, and we'll not be there before tomorrow night. If I were in his place I should be on hand at least a week beforehand. Just imagine what might happen in the meantime to delay one!"

"True. But it looks as if the boat were coming," Uncle Schenson observes, "and that is the only uncertain element. Besides, we have the railway."

"Let us hope that all will go smoothly," says Aunt Georgina.

But, obviously, she is uneasy, for she goes over to the guard and asks him if he does not think the boat is stopping rather long at Rottneros.

"I think, Frua, it will be lying there a good while longer," the guard says, laughing. "The boat brought a party of gentlemen from Karlstad who were going to pay their respects to the Squire of Rottneros.

There's no telling, Frua—they may be eating their breakfast at this time."

"The Squire of Rottneros?" Aunt Georgina repeats inquiringly. "By the bye, who owns Rottneros now?"

"A man named Wall—Gustaf Adolf Wall," the guard replies. "He's one of those men who is lord of all he surveys, he is!"

"Ah! Now I remember having heard of him," says Aunt Georgina. "But surely the steamer must make her calls even if Squire Wall gives his guests a farewell breakfast."

"Haw, haw, haw!" the guard roars. "It is clear that Frua has had no dealings with Wall. If the captain of that boat were to leave Rottneros without the Squire's guests, it would be the last time he'd stand on the commander's bridge of the *Anders Fryxell*."

"You don't say so! Oh, in that case I may as well go back to the woods and sit down."

Aunt Georgina then turns and walks up the hill and seats herself once more on the shelf of rock. Uncle Schenson and Uncle Oriel soon follow. Ernst, Klaës, Elin, and Allan remain on the pier, but Alma, Gerda, and I sit down on the rock with the grown-ups.

"I heard you ask the guard a moment ago who owns Rottneros," says Uncle Schenson. "It seems strange to find anyone who has not heard of G. A. Wall."

"Ah, then you regard him as a man of distinction?"
"Without doubt he is the most notable figure in Värmland. The way he has built up the works at Rottneros seems almost unbelievable. New buildings every year. He does not think in terms of utility only, but of beauty as well. The mansion itself has been remodelled, and I have been told that it is positively palatial. The gardens, too, and the parks, are well kept. Several times during my stay at Mårbacka I thought of driving over there, but I couldn't very well do so, as the families are not on visiting terms."

Uncle Oriel, who has not spoken since we left home, now puts in his oar. "Lieutenant Lagerlöf is quite right not to associate with G. A. Wall."

"True, they are not on the same financial footing," Uncle Schenson concedes. "But then Wall has no pride of riches."

"The blithering idiot," says Uncle Oriel. "Can't he see where he is heading for! The blockhead will be bankrupt within five years!"

"But, Oriel," Uncle Schenson protests, "he was a man of wealth even before the war, and during the present flourishing state of the market he is said to have grown fabulously rich. He has bought up all the old manufacturing estates in Sunne, and I've been informed that he already owns Lövstaholm, Bada, Torsby, Kristinefors, Stöpafors, and Öjervik."

Uncle Oriel, lying on the moss with his hat drawn

over his eyes, does not even bother to remove it as he answers:

"So he speculates in real estate, too—bankruptcy within four years!"

"Listen to me, Oriel," says Uncle Schenson, whose patience is becoming somewhat exhausted. "The man, I assure you, is no adventurer. For example, he is uncommonly generous to his employees. Just consider that at every worker's home at Rottneros a cow and a pig are slaughtered every autumn! And during the famine of 1868, when other people were eating bread made of ground bark, the workmen on the Rottneros estate were eating their fill of white bread and bacon."

Now Uncle Oriel actually takes off his hat and, rising on his elbow, says: "Aha! So he's prodigal as well—bankruptcy within three years!"

We children—Alma, Gerda, and I—can't understand why Uncle Oriel should say such things. We know that Squire Wall has as much power as if he owned Aladdin's lamp; he need only to wish for a thing to have it. We think Uncle Oriel only wants to tease Uncle Schenson; for he is given to ragging, and being quick-witted, he loves to tantalize people.

Uncle Schenson, however, goes right on defending G. A. Wall. "Consider the high esteem in which he is held. He has been chosen to stand for a member of the Riksdag."

"A multiplicity of interests!" Uncle Oriel fairly shouts in alarm. "He'll go into bankruptcy in two years!"

"You are too severe on the man, Oriel. People have the greatest confidence in his ability. He plans to take up the old project of joining Lake Fryken to Vänern by constructing a canal."

"So he is a canal builder, too! Bankruptcy within the year!"

Uncle Schenson makes no retort, but takes out his watch. "It is nearly one o'clock," he says. "I think I'll go down to the pier to see if the steamer will not be along soon."

Uncle Schenson goes halfway down the hill, then turns and comes back. "You do not stop to consider, Oriel, that if it turns out as you say, then not only Wall but the whole Fryken Valley will go down in the crash."

"I can't help that," says Uncle Oriel. "It will always be thus so long as the people do not learn to discriminate between responsible persons and adventurers."

"But what proof have you that Wall is an adventurer?"

"My dear Schenson, what proof do I need? I am many years older than you and have seen more of the world than you or anyone else here in Värmland. And I know that when a man gives breakfasts that last for hours while others are kept waiting—fearful of being late to their work—then, mark my words, that man is near his downfall."

I don't know whether Uncle Oriel is serious or merely jesting, but all the way home I keep thinking of what he has said.

XXII
THE WELL

We are sitting on the stoop at Mårbacka—everyone says we should call it veranda now, as "stoop" is so old-fashioned—hoping that Aunt Nana Hammargren will feel able to tell us a story this evening as she has done every evening since she came to Mårbacka. Aunt Nana has stayed a little longer than the other guests, that she might have a quiet visit with Mamma and Papa and Aunt Lovisa. We have had glorious weather while Aunt Nana has been here, so that we could sit outdoors until eleven o'clock in the evening. And she has sat on the steps with us children and told story after story.

Aunt Nana Hammargren has a lovely voice that brings the tears to our eyes when she tells of something beautiful. And Aunt Nana is beautiful herself, and happy, too, for she and Uncle Hammargren are a perfect match and very much in love with each other. We used to feel sorry for Aunt Nana because she has no daughters—only three sons; but she herself seems quite satisfied with what she has.

We children had counted on a story from Aunt Nana tonight also; but this morning she suddenly became ill. She was perfectly well before the post came and she began to read the *Värmland News*. She had no more than glanced at the paper when she said she had a severe headache and must go to her room and lie down.

I don't understand how one could get a headache from reading the *Värmland News*, for I have gone over it from the first page to the last and found nothing unusual. We have not seen Aunt Nana since, and fear there will be no story from her tonight.

But imagine our joy when Aunt Nana comes out on the porch and says she is better now. She sits down on the steps with us children; this time she tells us a true story that has been handed down.

It is nearly dark, but I can see that Aunt Nana is pale and her eyes are as red from weeping as mine were when I went to the ball in Sunne. But her voice was never more beautiful, and whatever she says, even the humorous things, somehow becomes strangely touching. I have to swallow hard to keep the tears from falling.

AUNT NANA'S STORY

This happened one summer when my parents were living. The housekeeper—the same Maja Persdotter who is here today—sat in the kitchen one morning pounding salt in a brass mortar, when a man came to the door and asked to see the Paymaster of the Regiment. The housekeeper replied that the paymaster was not at home, which was the truth. The man then asked if he could speak to Fru Lagerlöf.

"She is sick," said the housekeeper, which was also the truth; for my mother had suffered from toothache all night and was lying down on the sofa in the room adjoining the kitchen with a hot poultice on her cheek.

She thought the stranger would leave when he heard that, but instead he strode over to the low settle—which stood below the table-bed then as now —and, seating himself, stretched out his long legs.

"I wonder if Fru Lagerlöf will be able to see me if I wait awhile?" he said.

The housekeeper wanted to know the nature of his business with her master and mistress. The stranger informed her that he was a well digger; and as he had heard that the water at Mårbacka was poor he had come to dig a proper well. His name was Germund Germundsson—a name, he averred, that was known throughout all Värmland. He had dug

wells on almost every manorial estate in the province,
and everywhere he had brought forth good water;
so he knew that the owners had cause to remember
him with gratitude.

The housekeeper had never heard of the man and
his great renown. Observing him more closely, she
said to herself: "If the decision rested with me, he'd
get no work from my employers." The man was ex-
ceedingly tall and of powerful build, but his head was
noticeably small and narrow at the top. His eyes were
dark and piercing, his nose stood out like the beak
of a bird of prey, and he had a strong, pugnacious
chin. He was a person she wished to have out of the
house as quickly as possible.

"There have been many well diggers here, both in
the Paymaster's time and before it," she said. "They
ran about with willow branches, searching for water
veins on every hill, but for all that the drinking
water here was no better."

"They must have been poor wretches who didn't
know their business," said the man. "But it's different with me. You might at least let Fru Lagerlöf
know that I'm here."

But that was exactly what the housekeeper did
not intend to do. She knew better than anyone else
that the water at Mårbacka was bad. There was only
one well where they had water the year around—
even in the worst drought. But the water was so

turbid and brackish that it wasn't fit to drink. Clear water had to be brought every day from a cold spring that lay far from the house. But she would rather carry drinking water any distance than have aught to do with a tramp like Germund Germundsson.

"You needn't think you'll get me to call the mistress. She's got an aching tooth. I've just been in and put a hot poultice on her cheek, so I think she is sleeping now."

"Well, then," said the well digger, "there's nothing to do but wait until she wakes up."

He crossed his long legs and leaned against the back of the settle, to make himself as comfortable as possible. The housekeeper began to pound her mortar again. It was some time before either of them spoke. But at last the well digger broke the silence by asking her what she was pounding.

"Salt," she snapped.

"Oh, that is why your tongue is so dry!"

The housekeeper made no retort. She would not permit herself to bandy words with a facetious stranger. There was another interval of silence. Presently the kitchen door opened and two maids came in with a big cowlful of water, which they carried on a pole laid across their shoulders. It was a heavy burden, and their backs must have ached as they lowered the cowl to the floor before lifting it onto the trestletree which served as a rest.

As soon as the maids had put the water cowl in its place, the well digger arose and went over to have a look at the water. It was cloudier than usual, having just come from the well.

"Whew, what a mess!" he said and spat right into the water.

That was the most disgusting thing he could have done. Now the maids would have to pour out all the water and fetch another cowlful. To spit in the water, you know, children, is as wicked as tramping on bread.

The maids were furious at the man. One seized the cowlstaff and the other the big copper dipper, which hung on the side of the cowl, and went for him. "Clear out, you swine!" they shrieked at him. "What right have you here? You haven't got the manners of a decent hog."

The man was obliged to defend himself, and the uproar in the kitchen was deafening. In the midst of the fracas the door of the kitchen bedroom opened and Fru Lagerlöf appeared on the threshold.

"What on earth are you doing out here?" she asked.

They stopped at once. The stranger turned his back on the maids and greeted Mother respectfully. "It is not so serious as it looks, Frua," he said.

"This beast spat in the water cowl," the maids shrieked, pointing to the man.

"I had to resort to a bit of ribaldry to awaken Frua," the well digger explained. "But I'll soon make up for it."

Then, grasping the water cowl by the handles, he carried it out of the kitchen and emptied the water he had polluted upon the stone step outside the door.

Mother, the housekeeper, and the two maids looked on in speechless amazement at the strength of the man. But they were to have greater proof of his strength later! Germund Germundsson now gripped the handle of the cowl with one hand and swung it onto his shoulder as easily as if it were a mug of ale, and, carrying it down to the well, began to refill it with water.

When Mother saw what the man was doing, she quickly sent a maid out with the cowlstaff, but he did not need it, he said. Grasping again the cowl by the handles, he carried it at arm's length across the stableyard into the kitchen and set it down on the trestletree.

By this feat he had redeemed himself in the eyes of everyone, and it was clear that he would be allowed to dig as many wells as he wished at Mårbacka. One does not readily say no to a man who can lift the roof off your house if he were so minded. As soon as Mother assured him that he might dig the well, he asked her where she would like to have it.

"It must lie in a spot where there is water in the

ground," she said, "and as close as possible to the wash house, for it is there the water is most needed."

"If Frua wishes to have the well at the side of the wash house, that's where it's going to be," said Germund.

The following day he began digging just outside the wash house. No one had seen him go about with a divining rod or any other testing device. He seemed to be lord of all the water veins in the depths of the earth and could make them flow in whatever direction he saw fit.

He would have no help with the digging, but called for a couple of boys with wheelbarrows to remove the dirt and gravel he tossed up. He was a fast worker. Never in their lives had the boys been so driven! They had hardly got one barrow emptied before another was filled. Germund had staked off a space of about fifty square feet, and to dig that out was no slight task. But before evening he had dug down so far that not even his head was visible.

Mother used to say that while Germund was digging the well she couldn't sit quietly sewing, for she wanted to see whether he could find water. Besides, it was fun to watch him at his work. She wouldn't have believed that a person could be so strong or have such tenacity of purpose.

Germund was pleased with the ground where he dug. He declared that all signs indicated that he would soon strike water. He had found no stones or hardpan; but when he had cleared away the top layer he came upon dry sand, and by the time he had dug through that he would find water—of that he was certain.

But the gravel bed was deep, and Germund had to dig the next day also. The work did not go so fast now as on the previous day. He had to send for workmen to put up a shaft on which two men could stand to remove all the gravel he tossed up, and dump it at the side of the opening. But this device soon became inadequate. The excavation was now so deep that the men were obliged to rig up a pulley, on which two barrels attached to long ropes could be moved up and down, as ore is drawn from the mines.

Toward evening of the third day, Mother became uneasy. Germund was digging deeper and deeper into the earth; still, no water came. If Mother had known the work was to last so long she would never have undertaken it on her own initiative. She had hoped to surprise Father with this water, and now perhaps she had let herself in for something that could not be carried out successfully.

One day it rained, and water came pouring into the well from every direction. But it did not come from any well spring. It was surface water, which had to be bailed out; so it was some time before the well was dry.

Germund worked on and on. The men had to fetch a long ladder and lower it into the hole so that he could go up and down. But the ladder soon became too short, and they had to lengthen it with two additional ladders.

The worst of it was, they were in the midst of the harvest season. The hay was dry and should be taken in, and the rye was ripe and must be garnered. How to get the harvesting done, Mother did not know, for the farmhands were busy at the well from morning to night. All the other work was at a standstill.

Mother suggested to Germund that he stop digging; but he would not listen. Then she asked him if it would not be advisable to try digging in some other place, but this he positively refused to do. Mother was at her wit's end. She had the feeling that he was capable of doing no end of harm if he were not allowed to finish the work he had set his heart upon.

Mother noticed one day that the rye was turning brown, which is a sign that it was so ripe that the kernels were ready to drop out of their beards. It would not do to put off the cutting any longer. Father was up at the Kymsberg Ironworks, of which he was the manager. So he was not far away, and Mother could have sent for him easily; but she did not wish to unless it became absolutely necessary. It would have hurt her pride, I think, to be obliged to admit that she could not manage the farm herself.

But just when the need was greatest, she had an inspiration. She went out to the well and begged Germund to come up from the hole, as she wished to speak to him. When he came up he was covered from head to foot with mud and sand; so she could scarcely tell what he was made of.

Mother told him the rye must be cut next day and asked him to help with the work. The man threw up his big chin and grinned at her scornfully.

"Oh, I have cut rye in my day," he said with a lofty air, "but it is not the kind of work that is suitable for me."

"Nevertheless, rye is what we must all live upon," said Mother. "However much water we may get from your well, Germund, it will be of little use if we have no bread."

The well digger gave her a sharp glance from his dark eyes, but smiled rather indulgently, as if he were amused at a mere woman's daring to tell him the truth.

"Very well, Frua, it shall be as you wish. But I must have the longest scythe you've got on the farm, and plenty of hands to bind the rye."

That, Mother assured him, he should have. In the evening Germund inspected all the scythes on the farm, but found none that suited him. He actually withdrew his offer to help with the cutting. To expect a grown man to use such scythes! They were only toys for children to play with. So in the middle of the night Mother had to send for a smith to forge a scythe two yards long.

Mother was up next morning at four o'clock, when the farm labourers went to their work; for she feared Germund might offer some new objection. It was well she was on hand; otherwise he probably would have crawled out of his bargain.

Germund, carrying the scythe over his shoulder, came with the other harvesters. He walked at the head of the labourers and was the first to start working. But when he had swung the scythe two or three times he turned and looked back at the binders. And again he threatened to quit.

"What does this mean?" he demanded. "Am I to have only two binders? In that case, I may as well go home and lay me down to rest."

"These are two of the best binders we have on the farm," Mother informed him. But the well digger's only answer was a shrug.

"Oh," said Mother, "if it's nothing else that's wanting, I'll get you a binder who can work as fast as two men can cut. With the two you have now, perhaps that will be enough for you."

"Well, perhaps they'll do—if they're the right sort."

Mother hurried back to the house and went straight

to the kitchen. "I want you to go out and bind sheaves for that presumptuous fellow," she said to the housekeeper, "and show him what you can do. It may teach him to have a little respect for the Mårbacka folk."

So Maja Persdotter, who could bind sheaves for two cutters, went out to the rye fields at once. But Germund was able to give her and the two other binders all the work they could do.

So much rye had never been harvested at Mårbacka in a single day. When the other farmhands saw how rapidly Germund swung his scythe, they paused in their work and stared at him. Then, grasping their scythes, they went at the rye with a will, the blades falling before them like a shower of rain. And that was how the whole field was reaped in a single day.

It was a great relief to Mother to have the rye harvested, and so she thought Germund might as well be allowed to go back to his digging for a few days more. She soon found, however, that while Germund was at Mårbacka she would have no end of trouble and worry.

On the very day the rye was being reaped a strange young girl came to the house. She walked up the steps, entered the hall, and went straight to the kitchen. Since the housekeeper and the maids were out binding sheaves, Mother was alone in the house.

As the door opened she looked up and wondered who the girl might be.

She was dressed like a gentlewoman, but her clothes were threadbare and so ill fitting it was apparent they had not been made for her. She was about twenty years old, of slight build, and painfully thin, but her hands were large and rough like those of a labourer. She could not be called pretty, nor was she ugly, for her face was round and her complexion clear and rosy. When Mother wished to describe her she would always say: "She was one of those nondescript women you do not remember until you have seen her a number of times."

"I should like to speak to Fru Lagerlöf," said the girl.

"You are speaking to her," Mother replied.

The young girl came nearer. "I am Johanna Octopius, daughter of Dean Octopius of Brunskog," she said and held out her hand.

While Mother was shaking hands with her she tried to recall what she had heard about Dean Octopius and his family. Mother herself was a clergyman's daughter and related to all the clerical families in Värmland; so surely, she thought, she must know who the Octopiuses were.

"But is not Dean Octopius dead?" she queried.

"He is, alas!" sighed the girl. "I lost both father and mother many years ago."

It was all clear to Mother now. Dean Octopius and his wife died within a short time of each other and were survived by an only child—a little girl who was not quite like other children. As no relative had been found who could take the child, the poor thing had to remain with her father's successor in the capacity of a Cinderella. In return for her services she was given food, shelter, and such clothing as had been discarded. She was by no means a fool, yet it could not be said that she was blessed with sound common sense. Mother guessed at once that this was the same Johanna Octopius who had now come to Mårbacka. But what in the world was she doing here?

Johanna Octopius, however, was not long in stating her errand. She had come to ask Mother if she might stay here for a few days.

"It is not unlikely that you may," Mother told her, "but first I should like to know why you wish to stop here."

The poor girl flushed perceptibly—evidently she had not expected to be questioned. She stood nervously pulling at a finger, not knowing what to answer, for she was painfully shy. When at last she spoke, it was with an air of mystery and in a voice so low as to be almost inaudible:

"I was ordered to come here."

"Is there anyone here whom you wish to see?"

The girl looked even more distressed. "I have never

been able to lie," she said. "So I won't tell you if there's anyone here I want to see. I came to this house in answer to a command I received yesterday, to be on hand when I was needed."

Mother knew from her answer that the girl was not right in her head. She thought, however, it was best to let her stay at Mårbacka until there was an opportunity to send her home. Mother said: "Go into the room off the kitchen and rest yourself while I prepare the supper. You see, I have no servants in the house today; they are all out in the field binding sheaves."

Johanna Octopius said she was not tired and offered to help Mother get the supper. Mother soon found that, though the girl was willing, she was awkward and bungled everything she touched. She carried in wood and made up a fire, but she put so much salt in the porridge that no one could have eaten it; so it had to be thrown away, and the fresh pot of porridge she let burn.

At eight o'clock the men came into the kitchen to eat. Johanna Octopius stood at the stove dishing out the scorched porridge. When the well digger saw her he ripped out an oath, and Johanna Octopius dropped a big ladleful of the porridge on the fire. The smell of the burning porridge in the kitchen became insufferable. None of the men, however, exchanged a look or a word.

The following day the housekeeper informed
Mother that the well digger had told Lill-Bengt that
that crazy daughter of a clergyman had fallen in love
with him the spring he dug a well at Brunskog
Rectory. At first he was flattered, he had said, because a girl of the upper class had taken a fancy to
him, but after a while he hated the very sight of her.
She pursued him wherever he went, and he'd never
get rid of the girl unless he killed her.

Mother had suspected from the first that a love
affair lay behind the mysterious call. Now that the
mystery was solved, Mother ordered Lill-Bengt to
get ready at once and drive Mamselle Octopius back
to Brunskog. Then she talked to the girl and tried
to make her realize how unseemly her behaviour was.
Did she not see that she was lowering herself by
running after a man who did not want her? And,
finally, she told the girl that she must go home and
that it would not be worth her while to come back.

Johanna Octopius bent before the storm of reproof
like the frail reed that she was. Without a protest she
seated herself in the cart and drove away from Mårbacka.

When Lill-Bengt had driven about two miles, one
of the pegs that fastened the traces to the harness
came loose, and he had to get down to tighten it. He
was only a moment, but in the meantime Johanna
Octopius seized the opportunity to make her escape.

Before the driver discovered her flight, she had disappeared in the woods near by. He tried to catch her, but on account of the horse he could not go very far. And so she eluded him.

To steal away and disappear, to run like water one tries to hold between the hands, was the only thing the girl could do to perfection—and she must have practised at that all her life.

Lill-Bengt had to turn around and drive back to Mårbacka. As Johanna Octopius did not appear again that day, Mother wondered if the poor girl had done herself some harm. She was sorry now that she had spoken harshly to her.

The next morning the runaway came into the cow barn and asked for a glass of milk. While she was drinking it the dairymaid quietly sent for the mistress; but when Mother came out to speak to Johanna she had already gone.

The well digger was in a rage. One side of the shaft had collapsed, filling the opening with sand. Whenever that crazy Hanna appeared, things always went wrong with him, he said. He never in his life had laid violent hands upon anyone, but if that woman continued to pursue him he would have to rid himself of her some way or other.

Mother was sure that something dreadful would happen. She had had that feeling from the first day Germund came to the house. She wrote to the dean of Brunskog, begging him to send for the girl; but to no avail. Then she tried to capture her in order to shut her up. But the girl was on her guard and took to her heels the moment anyone approached.

One day Johanna Octopius came stealing across the yard and up to the well hole; she stopped and peered down into the deep excavation. Germund, who was down at the bottom of the well, must have felt her presence, for in a moment he appeared at the top of the ladder, shrieking and cursing. Although she fled instantly, he hurled stones and gravel after her as if she had been a mangy cur. Johanna Octopius, however, was not to be frightened away; she stole about the grounds as before.

And then one morning, when there had been about all the mishaps that could possibly occur during the digging of a well, when the hole was so deep that one who stood at the bottom could see the stars moving across the sky, though on the surface it was broad day: then one morning a man came dancing into the kitchen shouting: "Water! Water!"

Mother, the housekeeper, and the maids ran out. They bent over the well, peering into its depths, and, sure enough, far down at the bottom of the hole they beheld a shining mirror of water.

There is something almost miraculous about finding water in that way on a farm. Mother had had a trying time and had often wished she had never ordered the digging. But now that water had come, she thanked God from her heart for this great blessing. Then she asked after Germund.

"He is still down there," answered one of the men. "Maybe he wants to see first whether it's a real water vein he has struck."

They called down to him, but he did not answer. One of the men was about to descend to see whether anything had happened to him, when Germund placed his foot on the lowest rung of the ladder.

He mounted slowly, feeling for the rungs with one hand and holding the other hand to his eyes. They thought he had got sand in his eyes.

When he reached the top rung he put out his hand gropingly. Two men sprang to his aid. It was almost impossible to get him on solid ground again. He had only to put out his foot and take a step, the men told him, but he was afraid.

"My dear Germund, we are so glad that you have found water," said Mother.

"Ah, Frua, that water was dearly bought! Just as the water gushed forth down there, something that felt like smoke flew into my eyes. And now I can't see."

When they finally had him on firm ground, he threw himself down on the grass and pressed both hands against his eyes. The men stood silent, waiting for him to rise. None of them liked him, but they thought it dreadful if he should lose his sight.

In a moment he rose to a sitting posture. "There's still the same darkness," he said. "It is all over with me, for I am blind."

Mother tried to reassure him. "It will soon pass," she said. "You were down there in the dark too long, and you have not yet become accustomed to the daylight."

"No, it isn't that," he said. "My eyes burn as though they were on fire. Oh, what is to become of me!"

With that he leaped to his feet, raised his arm high, and tried to jump into the well. The men rushed forward and barred his way, but he flung them all aside.

"Let me be!" he roared. "I want to die down there!"

It was horrible! The men tried to restrain him, and in the struggle he lost his sense of direction and ran round and round in circles, shrieking and cursing and clutching at the air as if trying to capture someone.

"Show me where the well lies," he shouted, "or I'll crush the life out of the first man I lay my hands on."

He raved like a madman, but luckily no tragedy occurred, for the people ran out of his way, and he himself, fortunately, got nowhere near the well. Again he threw himself down on the grass. Every part of his body twitched and jerked convulsively, and, clenching his fists, he broke out again and again into wild threats.

While he lay there in a rage so menacing that no man would have dared go near him, the half-witted girl, Johanna Octopius, approached. She came in her usual quiet way, so that no one was aware of her presence until she was close beside him.

Mother was about to rush forward to warn her, but she had already laid her hand on his.

"Don't curse so, Germund," she said in her low, soft voice. "I am here to help you."

Everyone thought that he would seize her by the throat and choke her to death. He suddenly burst into a horrible, savage laugh, but he did not harm her.

"I am here," she said again. " *They* knew this would happen, and *They* sent me here. I was born into this world for no other purpose than to help you."

There must have been something about her that did him good, for he took her hands and laid them against his burning eyes.

"Thou mad Hanna!" he said. "Oh, thou mad Hanna!"

"What does it matter that you are blind?" she said. "I will be eyes to you."

In his misery and utter helplessness, it was a comfort to know there was someone who cared for him, whether he was blind or seeing, weak or strong, good or bad, rich or poor.

Mother, meanwhile, remained close by. She was not quite sure how this would end, when she heard Germund say:

"It is soothing to have your hand on my eyes."

Then Mother felt easy in her mind and beckoned the others to come away and leave them alone. You see, she knew that a great miracle had taken place. Love had found the way. It was God's will from the beginning that those two should be together.

When we have thanked Aunt Nana for telling us the story of the well, we say that the good water really deserved to have a story of its own.

"You have a wonderful memory, Nana," Aunt Lovisa remarks, "to be able to recall so many of Mother's old stories! I recollect, of course, her telling us that the man who dug the well went blind, but his name and all the details I had quite forgotten."

Papa also says that Aunt Nana is wonderful. "But are you quite certain that the girl's name was Octopius? It sounds so unfamiliar."

Aunt Nana laughs. "You are right, that was not the girl's real name; as I did not wish to give her right name, I invented a fictitious one."

"As every true narrator should, to be sure," Papa observes.

"But, Nana, what made you think of that particular story tonight?" Mamma queries.

"Well, you see"— Aunt Nana drawls a bit— "it is rather difficult to explain. Perhaps it was because I've heard so much talk about the pond the last few days——"

Elin Laurell now puts a query: "Do you really believe, Fru Hammargren, that love always leads us aright? Should not one first question it critically instead of accepting it blindly?"

Aunt Nana ponders a long moment before she answers:

"I believe that love invariably leads us aright. Fröken Laurell. But it takes great courage and faith to obey its promptings, and that, alas, is what we all lack."

Papa usually keeps all the Värmland papers in a small cupboard at the back of his writing table. The next day he asks me to put away the paper Aunt Nana was reading before she got her bad headache. While I am folding the paper, I see on the front page two or three round blotches that look like dried-in tears. I verily believe the newspaper, the headache, and the story are somehow linked together, but in what way I do not know. And because I am so young, no one will tell me. So now I think I shall never know.

XXIII
THE MARKET FAIR

We have had so much to do, ever since the day Aunt Nana Hammargren left. There have been two or three days of hop-picking, bee-killing, and apple-gathering, besides the summer's washing and the baking of *knäckebröd*. We have dipped wax for candles, brewed unfermented beer, grated potato meal, and made a whole kegful of cider. I don't know how Aunt Lovisa, the housekeeper, and the maids ever managed to get through with it all in so short a time. But of course we children have spent every spare moment in the kitchen, helping with the work.

Then, too, we have had sheep slaughter and killing of pigeons. There are more than a hundred pigeons to feed every day, which is a little too many. But the day the pigeons are to be killed is the worst of all, for it always puts Papa in bad humour. Although he knows it is necessary to reduce their number, he loves so much to see the pigeons about the place that he would rather the hawks devoured them than that we eat them.

All this work must be done in September, before the opening of the big market fair, the first Friday in October. By that time the house must be scoured and cleaned throughout and the storm windows set in, so that on Market Eve—as we call the day before the fair opens—the house is as clean and tidy from cellar to garret as at Christmas and Easter. Market Eve seems to me the most memorable day of the whole year. It is so quiet and restful everywhere. There are new rag carpets in every room, and the copper vessels have been polished until they shine like red gold. With the storm windows in, the house is cozy and warm, and everybody is amiable and full of happy expectation.

September has been a busy month for Papa also. He has had Inspector Nyman here, and the two have sat in the office making up the annual accounts. Papa has brought home big rolls of bills from the bank in Karlstad, and now, on Market Eve, he pays all his employees their yearly wage in full. Lars of London is the first to step into the office, and after him—one by one—come the other labourers. Next, in their order, come the farm bailiff, the stableman, the stableboy, and the boy who tends the sheep. When they have been paid, it is the turn of the housekeeper and all the maidservants, and the last one to receive hers is the governess. No—at the very last, we children step into the office and we receive a riksdaler each to spend next day at the fair.

The housekeeper never takes out any of her money; she merely asks Papa to deposit the sum in the savings bank to her credit. But the maids, with their crisp new banknotes in hand, come out from the office, rosy and smiling. Afterwards, they spend the whole evening discussing what they should buy at the fair. Nurse Maja tells Mamma that she has decided to purchase a pair of black kid gloves to wear when she goes to church.

"But, Maja, kid gloves are expensive," says Mamma, "and you would look just as fine in a pair of black thread mitts."

Toward evening there is life and movement out in the road. There are far-come marketfolk, peasants from Ransäter and Ullerud, even from Råda and Ekshärad, who had set out in time to be on hand when the fair opened; a long procession of foot-farers and drivers, nearly all bringing horses or cows, goats or sheep to sell at the fair. Watching the animals is the amusing part of the parade. The people we care nothing about, for they either walk or drive along the road slowly and perform no tricks, but the he-goats and the rams and the bull calves and the young colts evidently regard this tramp as a great frolic and cut up all kinds of capers.

We children and Elin Laurell have gone out on the avenue to see the procession of marketfolk pass by. After a while Papa joins us, and then the fun begins. Papa immediately hails the passers-by. He wants to know where they come from and what they ask for their livestock. A man shouts back that he has a fine colt which the Lieutenant ought to buy, and a woman tearfully relates that the frost has killed the grain on her farm and that now she must part with this pretty heifer, which she has striven for two years to raise, in order to get money to buy food for the winter for herself and her children. Horse traders come driving their small carts, with a long line of horses in tow, to trade at the fair for others. Their animals look sleek and spirited; but Papa says one should never swap horses with a blackleg, as he invariably drugs them with arsenic, or whatever it is that makes them look fine for a day; but afterwards they collapse like boards loosely put together.

It is the first time that Elin Laurell has been at Mårbacka during the Åmbergshed fair, and she is astonished that we celebrate it as a great event. But she, too, finds it interesting; for she has never seen anything of the kind before. Turning to Papa, she says:

"Marketfolk must have passed this way every autumn for many, many years, and the owners of Mårbacka must have stood here chatting with them, as you are doing now. Do you know, Lieutenant, I feel as if I were living in another century, hundreds of years ago."

"I daresay you think it has been like this always," says Papa, "but I can tell you that the Åmbergshed fair of today is not what it was when I was young. In those days Mårbacka was like a veritable posting station. Merchant Kjellin of Åmål, the husband of my sister Caroline, used to come with several wagon-loads of goods, and he and his clerks would stay here nights during the fair—which lasted at least a week. And one after another, my father's friends and acquaintances would come and beg us to take them in. For often enough they had no better place to sleep than in their wagons. Moreover, there was a certain fellowship among the gentry of the Fryken Valley in those days, and it was understood among us that each family, in turn, was to feed all the travellers at an old building that stood in the middle of the fair grounds and was known as the *Schalong*. And let me tell you there was no little anxiety for my mother when her turn came to feed the multitude! For, you see, at that time the leading merchants of Karlstad,

Filipstad, Kristinehamn, and Åmål went the rounds of the fairs with their goods themselves, and they wanted rich and well-prepared dishes. But nowadays. when we have these everlasting country stores, the delightful old customs have been abolished."

We begin to feel chilly from standing so long, and walk awhile to get warm. Papa, of course, goes with us, for he dare not stand still too long in the cold air of an autumn evening. He and Elin walk side by side, and he talks to her of the Åmbergshed fair of old and its glories. He tells many amusing anecdotes of those days. When he comes to the long dark road leading to the rectory, Papa stops.

"It is a strange coincidence," he says. "You remarked awhile ago that I and the others who have lived at Mårbacka must have walked here on the eve of the fair and talked with the marketfolk. And at this moment I can see my father as it were before me, as I saw him standing here one Market Eve. Though —when I come to think back—it was not on Market Eve itself, but it had some connection with the fair."

Papa lifts his hat and passes his hand across his brow, as if to clear his mind.

"Ah!" he says. "Now I remember what I wanted to tell you. We had gone out, Father, Sister, and I, to see the marketfolk, for this was Father's custom, the same as it is mine. But it was not on a Market Eve, nor could it have been on the opening day, as

Father had gone to Sunne that day on business. So it must have been in the evening of the second day, when many had made their purchases and gone home."

"Did this happen when you were a small boy?" Elin queries.

"No, Fröken Laurell. I was in my twenties then, and so was Nana. What kept me at home that autumn, I can't remember; for, as a rule, I was out on land-surveying expeditions. But perhaps it was because my father was growing old and needed someone to help him make up his accounts. His business interests were more extensive than mine, you see. But to get back to my story—when we had been standing awhile watching the wayfarers we began to feel chilly and walked toward the north, as we are doing now. Nana and Father walked arm in arm. They were always good comrades, and I think, of all his children, she was the one he loved best."

"She must have been a beautiful girl," says Elin.

"Indeed she was! And she was lively and full of fun. The old man always enjoyed her company. Let me see—this must have been in the early 'forties, before Nana was married or even betrothed. I remember it quite well because my parents had told me they were uneasy about her. As the rector at Halla was too old to carry on his pastoral duties, he had engaged an assistant, a young, good-looking chap.

Both Father and Mother noticed that he was setting his cap for Nana and that she was falling in love with him. The old folks had nothing against the curate. He was a gifted man and an excellent preacher; but rumours had reached them at various times that he was a hard drinker, and they did not want to give their daughter in marriage to a man of that sort."

"I should say not!" exclaims Elin in horror.

"Curious how things long buried in memory come back to one," says Papa. "I don't recollect exactly what we were talking about—Father, Nana, and I— as we walked here, but I know what we were thinking. All three of us were wondering whether the curate had come back from the fair. Father had been there on the opening day and thought then that the curate had been drinking. We knew he had come home the previous evening, and as we walked toward the rectory we wondered if he was safe at home now, or if he was still staggering about the streets of Sunne. But, naturally, we kept our thoughts to ourselves, for this was a delicate subject with us."

"It was not a very pleasant stroll, I fancy," says Elin Laurell.

"No, I can't say that it was. Nana, I thought, looked troubled. She chatted and jested as usual with Father, but it sounded forced. I helped to make conversation as best I could, though it was a bit laboured. We stopped to exchange a few words with some passer-by. (Father had lived at Mårbacka some forty years, and everyone hereabouts knew him.) Then we walked on, past the rectory, and stopped here, on this very road."

Papa looks about and points with his stick at the tall, dark spruces that border the road.

"It was as dark and dismal here then as it is to-day," he says, "or perhaps still more so; for the trees, I think, were taller then, and the road was narrower and steeper. As we stood here, a vehicle swung round the bend below, and we recognized the rector's horse and driver. We knew at once what kind of errand he was out on. The rector had sent him to find the curate and bring him home. It was Saturday evening, and the curate had to sleep off the effects of his debauch so that he could preach on Sunday."

"Oh, I say, Lieutenant, this is becoming positively thrilling," says Elin Laurell.

"Thrilling!" Papa echoes the word with contempt. "You use such queer expressions nowadays. I thought it appalling when I saw only the driver on the seat of the cart. We all feared that he had not been able to find the curate. Nana went white as a sheet, and I had never seen such scorn and loathing on Father's face as I saw that day. As the cart drew nearer, Father caught a glimpse of a dark form lying on the floor of the cart. He signalled the driver to stop.

"'So you found him, Ola,'" he said.

"'Yes, Paymaster, I've got him with me. But, Lord, he's a sight to behold!'

"Ola leaned back as he spoke and removed the hat which covered the curate's face. We stood so close that we could not help seeing him. Nana quickly averted her eyes and would have run away if Father had not caught her by the wrist and held her.

"'Look at him!' he said and drew her nearer, forcing her to look upon the curate, who lay there in a drunken stupor and covered with filth. He was so changed as to be almost beyond recognition.

"'Look at him!' Father again commanded. 'It will be well for you to do so. God pity the woman who marries that man!' I hardly think Nana obeyed Father, for she did not raise her eyes until he released her hand and told the servant to drive on."

"How cruel!" says Elin Laurell.

"Yes, I suppose it was. But you must remember that Father had a daughter who was married to Wachenfeldt, and he didn't want Nana, who was the apple of his eye, to go the same way. But Nana, both grieved and angry, walked in silence a few steps ahead of Father and me all the way home. Father looked stern, but I could see, all the same, that he was pleased. Without doubt, he thought it was well that Nana had got her eyes opened."

As Papa says this, he turns abruptly and walks

toward home with Elin by his side, and the two continue their conversation.

"How extraordinary!" says Elin. "I never would have believed that Fru Hammargren had been in love with anyone but her husband."

"Perhaps she was not very seriously in love with that parson," says Papa. "At least, she didn't mourn for him long. The fair was still on, and my brother-in-law, Kjellin, was stopping with us at the time. After talking things over with Father and Mother, they agreed to let Nana go back with him to Åmål and spend the winter with Caroline. While there, Nana met Tullius Hammargren, who was head-master of a boys' school at Åmål, and when she came home, in the spring, the two were engaged."

Elin asks no more questions, but I am impatient to learn what to me is the most important of all. "But, Papa, what became of the curate?"

"Ah!" he says, surprised. "Little pitchers have ears, I see. I'm sorry to tell you that he went from bad to worse. He drank heavily and ended his days in the asylum. I don't know how it happened, but there are some who say that he lost his mind because Nana would have nothing more to do with him."

I think it is so romantic that a man has gone mad with love for my Aunt Nana. If I had only dared I would have asked many more questions.

Afterwards I beg Elin to ask Papa what Aunt Nana had read in the newspaper that day, in the summer, and why she had told us the story of the well on that particular day. But Elin says she will do no such thing. She thinks it isn't nice to be so curious.

XXIV
THE "EARTHQUAKE"

AT TWELVE o'clock, when our morning lessons are over, we always run downstairs to see Mamma. She usually sits at the small table by the window, sewing. While we watch her at her work, she will ask whether we know our lessons and whether we have been diligent and well behaved; and of course we always answer, "Yes."

That day I had finished a little before the others, and, after washing my slate and putting my books away, without waiting for Anna or Gerda, I hurried down to Mamma's room. When I opened the door, I did not find her in her usual place at the sewing table. She was pacing up and down the room and sobbing.

She did not weep as though she had received news of a death, but as if she were beside herself with anger and despair. Pressing her hands to her head, she cried in a voice so shrill it cut into my ears:

"He must not do it! He must not do it!"

I stand stock-still in the doorway, unable to take a step. I would never have thought that Mamma could cry like that. The floor seems to open before me, and the whole house rocks to and fro.

Had Papa or Aunt Lovisa been weeping so violently it wouldn't have been very alarming. But Mamma would never weep like that unless we were threatened with ruin; for she is so wise, and the one on whom we can always depend.

Papa sits at the writing table, following Mamma with his eyes. He too looks troubled, though not in the same way as Mamma. He tries to say something to quiet her, but she does not hear him.

When Papa sees me standing at the door, he rises quickly and comes over to me. Taking my hand, he says: "We must go now and let Mamma compose herself." Then, leading me into the dining room, he drops wearily into the rocker, while I stand close beside him.

"Why is Mamma crying?" I ask.

Papa does not answer me at once, for he sees that I am frightened. Perhaps he thinks it would be cruel to say that this is something I could not understand.

"Your Uncle Kalle came here this morning to tell us he would have to sell Gårdsjö."

This is sad news to me as well as to my parents, for I love the place and my cousins who live there.

Gårdsjö has always been to me a second home. Yet I cannot understand why Mamma should take the loss so hard.

"You know that your mother is deeply attached to Gårdsjö. The foundry estate was not so extensive at the time your maternal grandfather bought it. He had made a fortune in trade at Filipstad; but as the owner of a foundry estate, he and his family had quite a different social standing."

I have nothing to say, so I keep silence.

"My father-in-law was obliged to run up to Gårdsjö twice a year," Papa continues, "and his eldest daughter usually accompanied him. That was how we met, your mother and I."

I know, of course, what Papa will say—Mamma has many happy memories that endear the place to her; but it is not like Mamma to cry so bitterly because of bright memories.

"When we were married," Papa goes on to say, "we lived at Gårdsjö for the first few years—until my father's death, when we came to live at Mårbacka."

I shake my head. I do not see what all this has to do with Mamma's weeping.

"Don't you understand that your mother thinks it deplorable that your uncle should sell Gårdsjö?"

"Yes. But why must Uncle Kalle sell?"

"He says he's losing money every year he lives

there. The forge, as you know, was shut down some time ago, and the soil does not yield enough to live upon. Mamma thinks that with the sawmill, the brickyard, and the flour mill, he ought to be able to manage. But he cannot count on them, as we are in for a long period of hard times."

I close my eyes, and I seem to feel the earth tremble. One after another of the great manorial estates crumble. Now Rottneros is falling, now Skarped, now Öjervik, Stöpafors, Lövstafors, Gylleby, and Helgeby. Herrestad has already fallen, and Gårdsjö is tottering. I begin to sense what it is that Mamma fears.

As I stand there with closed eyes, Papa touches my hand.

"Go into the parlour, like a good girl, and open the door to the bedroom a trifle, to see whether Mamma has quieted down."

I go, of course, but I can't help wondering why Papa does not go himself. I know that he hates to see anyone weep, but still, he should try to comfort Mamma. I had the feeling, when I stood at the bedroom door a moment ago, that Papa was actually glad of an excuse to escape. Papa is rather helpless in some things.

And now that I am alone in the parlour, I understand why Mamma is crying. I remember what Aunt Georgina said: Mamma is worried because Papa is

/

too ill to undertake any active work. Mamma knew
that bad times were coming, and had hoped and believed that Uncle Kalle would be a help and a stay
to her when Papa could no longer be. But now that
Uncle Kalle is leaving Gårdsjö, Mamma stands
alone, with no one to go to for advice or help.

As I open the door of the bedroom, I see Anna
there. She has made Mamma lie down on the sofa
and is spreading a shawl over her.

"Mamma is in good hands," I say to myself and
go back to the dining room to tell Papa.

And now I see for the first time how old and broken
Father is. I only wish I were rich and powerful, so
that I could help him!

THE BOOKS OF
SELMA LAGERLÖF
Brief Descriptive Notes

THE STORY OF GÖSTA BERLING

THE saga of a drunken preacher, poet, "lord of 10,000 kisses and 13,000 love letters," a heroic scamp whose adventures are the theme of many a Swedish legend. One of the great romantic novels of our time.

INVISIBLE LINKS

OLD Swedish legends, tales of simple peasants and fisher folk.

THE MIRACLES OF ANTICHRIST

A MIRACLE story of Sicily, of the image of the Christ child and the false image that worked wonders in the name of Antichrist.

FROM A SWEDISH HOMESTEAD

A NOVELETTE, "From a Swedish Homestead," set in the northern woods, and nine shorter stories all laid in Sweden except "The Fisherman's Ring" and "Santa Catarina of Siena."

JERUSALEM

"JERUSALEM kills," said the Swedish proverb. In 1899–1900 Miss Lagerlöf journeyed to Palestine to learn the fate of the unhappy Dalecarlians who had made a pilgrimage to settle in the Holy Land. This is the story of "Little" Ingmar Ingmarsson who wins his title "Big" Ingmar before he sets out for Jerusalem. It ranks with Miss Lagerlöf's two greatest novels, *Gösta Berling* and *The Emperor of Portugallia.*

THE HOLY CITY, JERUSALEM II

THE Dalecarlian pilgrims meet a dramatic and pitiful fate in the Holy Land.

CHRIST LEGENDS

OLD and modern legends of Christ collected and retold.

THE WONDERFUL ADVENTURES OF NILS
THE FURTHER ADVENTURES OF NILS

COMMISSIONED by the Swedish school authorities, Miss Lagerlöf wrote these two books to keep alive the rich store of folklore and historic tradition that are the background of Swedish life. They have become children's classics throughout the world.

THE GIRL FROM THE MARSH CROFT

A NOVELETTE and eight shorter tales, one of which, "The Story of a Story," is a particularly interesting account of the writing of *Gösta Berling.*

LILJECRONA'S HOME

LILJECRONA was the musician who frittered away his time with Gösta Berling and the roistering cavaliers at Ekeby. In this book Liljecrona finds peace for his restless, storm-swept soul.

THE EMPEROR OF PORTUGALLIA

ONE of Miss Lagerlöf's great novels, the drama of Jan, the toil-worn clod, transformed by his love and faith in his daughter, young Glory Goldie Sunnycastle, the Godchild of the Sun.

THE TREASURE

A GRIM and romantic old Swedish legend of the ice-bound treasure of Mr. Arne.

THE OUTCAST

SVEN ELVERSON, outcast because he is accused of having eaten human flesh, finds rehabilitation in a great love.

MÅRBACKA

THE story of Miss Lagerlöf's childhood into which is woven the legends of her family. One of the most beautiful autobiographies of all time.

CHARLOTTE LÖWENSKÖLD

THE romantic love of a brilliant, unconventional aristocrat of the Napoleonic era and a vivid picture of Swedish society. Three Löwensköld stories, "The General's Ring," "Charlotte Löwensköld," and "Anna Svard," are published in America in one volume, *The Ring of the Löwenskölds.*

MEMORIES OF MY CHILDHOOD

THE second volume of Miss Lagerlöf's autobiography. The wistful, happy, tragic incidents of the family life written very simply as a child would tell them, not as a grown-up would remember them. With *Mårbacka* it makes one of the most original and beautiful of modern autobiographies.